OXFORD *Playscripts*

Series editors: Steve Barlow and Steve Skidmore

Bawden   *adapted by Robert Staunton*

Carrie's War

Oxford University Press, Great Clarendon Street, Oxford OX2 6DP

Oxford New York
Athens Auckland Bangkok Bogota Bombay
Buenos Aires Calcutta Cape Town Dar es Salaam
Delhi Florence Hong Kong Istanbul Karachi
Kuala Lumpur Madras Madrid Melbourne
Mexico City Nairobi Paris Singapore
Taipei Tokyo Toronto Warsaw

and associated companies in
Berlin Ibadan

Oxford is a trade mark of Oxford University Press

Printed and bound in Great Britain at Cambridge University Press

The publishers would like to thank the following for permission to
reproduce photographs:
p 82 Popperfoto; p 84 Hulton Deutsch Collection; pp 92/93 Keith
Thomson Photography

Illustrations are by Robert Goldsmith

Cover illustration by Simon Fell

Contents

Characters

* * * * * * * * * * * * * *

*In order of their
appearance on stage:*

Adult Carrie	*Carrie Willow as a grown woman*
Carrie	*Carrie Willow, an eleven-year-old girl, evacuated with her brother to the Evanses' house in Wales*
Hepzibah Green	*housekeeper to Mrs Gotobed at Druid's Bottom*
Albert Sandwich	*a fourteen-year-old evacuee living at Druid's Bottom*
Mrs Willow	*Carrie and Nick's mother*
Nick	*Nicholas Willow, Carrie's younger brother, aged nine.*
Teacher	*in charge of the evacuees (female)*
Auntie Lou	*Miss Louisa Evans, she keeps house for her brother Samuel Evans and is bullied by him*
Mr Evans	*Samuel Isaac Evans, grocer. A mean, god-fearing man*
Customers	*in Mr Evans's shop (non-speaking)*
Mrs Gotobed	*Mrs Dilys Gotobed, invalid elder sister of Mr Evans and Auntie Lou. She owns Druid's Bottom*
Major Cass Harper	*an American soldier, a friend of Auntie Lou's*

A Note on the Set

The set of the play consists of objects that you might find in an attic: discarded furniture; old junk; childhood belongings; forgotten for many years, but all of which have stories to tell and memories to evoke. These attic items should be arranged towards the back of the stage. This area is one of dark shadows and half-light. The characters in the play wait unseen in the shadows for their entrances onto the acting areas and return to their places in this part of the 'attic' when they exit. The areas of half-light allow some of the characters to watch and/or share their thoughts with the audience without interfering with the action of the play. Large and small props can be collected and replaced from the array of attic 'junk' as required.

To the front of the stage are three acting areas: a main acting area centre stage, and two other acting areas stage left and stage right. The area stage left is set with a chair. This area can be used to represent the downstairs room of the Evanses' house, the kitchen at Druid's Bottom and Mrs Gotobed's bedroom. The area stage right is set with Adult Carrie's trunk. This area can also be used to represent Carrie and Nick's bedroom at the Evanses' and the library at Druid's Bottom.

The character of Adult Carrie remains on stage throughout the play. She has two bases: a chair stage left where she can sit and rest or read from her diary; and a trunk stage right which contains a number of props which help her to remember her time as an evacuee in Wales. However, she is free to move about the stage as required, interacting with the characters from her childhood, sharing her memories with the audience or just watching the action as she relives her past.

In the novel of **Carrie's War**, Mister Johnny has a speech disability and has to be cared for by Hepzibah. In any production, it is best not to attempt a realistic portrayal of his character. A tailor's dummy wearing a coat can stand in for Mister Johnny, and can be moved around the stage when required. (See Scene 5, page 35.)

An asterisk (*) in the text indicates that ideas for staging that part of the playscript may be found in the Activities section on page 95. The use of quotation marks in stage directions, for example, Carrie 'looks at the embroidered picture' indicates that the action is mimed and the object involved is imaginary.

Scene 1

Lights up. **Adult Carrie** *is kneeling by an old tin truck, stage right, sifting through its contents, taking out and rearranging what is in there. Occasionally she throws something into a waste bin. She takes a cardboard box out of the trunk – it is for storing a gas mask. She does not open it immediately. It is as though she dare not look inside, perhaps she even wants to hide it from herself. She holds the box against herself and looks thoughtful.*
Carrie *runs out from the shadows and stands staring, immobile and frightened like a rabbit trapped by a car headlight.* **Hepzibah Green** *steps forward from the shadows.*

Hepzibah	(*In a soothing voice*) Poor old Carrie, she believed in my old tales.
Carrie	(*Hysterically*) It's on fire! The house is on fire! Blazing away, flames and smoke! They'll all be dead and it's all my fault!
	Albert Sandwich *steps forward from the shadows.*
Albert	She wasn't a witch, just good at guessing.
Carrie	All my fault! The happy times have ended.
Hepzibah	Maybe it was caused by Mister Johnny playing with matches. That's what the insurance man said.

Hepzibah, Albert and Carrie move back into the shadows. Adult Carrie shakes her head, as though trying to rid herself of a persistent memory.

Adult Carrie   (*Sadly*) So long ago. It all happened so long ago.

There is the sound of an air-raid siren quietly in the background. Adult Carrie strains to hear it and then takes the gas mask out of its box.

Adult Carrie   And I never ever had to use this gas mask. Not in Wales. No air raids there, just mountains and coal heaps. (*Pause*) Evacuated to Wales.

Adult Carrie puts the gas mask back in its box and puts it down. She then takes a pile of letters and a notebook or diary out of the trunk. As she does this Mrs Willow and Carrie step forward from the shadows.

Adult Carrie   Nineteen thirty-nine. England was at war with Germany. Evacuation. People were afraid that the German bombers would destroy London and the other large cities, so thousands of children were separated from their parents and sent to the countryside for safety. Evacuation. Sent away.

Mrs Willow   (*To Carrie*) It's too dangerous to stay in London, darling. You and Nicholas are going to be evacuated.

The air-raid siren is heard again.

Carrie   What's that?

Mrs Willow   It's an air-raid warning.

Carrie   What does it mean?

Mrs Willow   England is at war and what with Daddy gone back to his ship, and Mummy working, helping to win the war, you and Nicholas have to be safe. So, for a short while, you and Nicholas are going to live with someone else.

Carrie	Do we have to? I don't mind the air raids. I'm not frightened.

Adult Carrie opens the diary.

Adult Carrie	Nineteen thirty-nine. Evacuation. All so long ago but I can't forget.
Carrie	What about the grown-ups? Won't they need to be safe?
Mrs Willow	I'm going to work away from London so everyone will be all right.

Mrs Willow freezes. Carrie moves back into the shadows. Adult Carrie puts down the diary and picks up the gas mask box and a carrier bag with a broken string handle and places them in the centre of the stage. She returns and closes the trunk.

Adult Carrie	We weren't told where we were going. Just told to turn up at our schools, with a packed lunch and a change of clothes, then we went to the station with our teachers. Nick was with me.

Carrie steps forward from the shadows carrying two cases and places them near the carrier bag. She is wearing an identity label around her neck. She picks up the gas mask box and hangs it over her shoulder. Nick steps forward from the shadows and joins her. He is carrying his gas mask over his shoulder, and is wearing a label too. They are at a railway station. The sound of a steam train is heard. Carrie and Nick sit on the cases as though they are seats on the train. Mrs Willow moves back into the half-light. She waves to the children.

Mrs Willow	Sheep and mountains. It'll be such fun. Living in the country instead of the stuffy old city. You'll love it, see if you don't.

She moves back into the shadows. Nick is sick.

Adult Carrie	On the journey Nick threw up all over the teacher's skirt. Being sick was his own fault.
Carrie	(*To Nick*) You've been stuffing your face ever since we left London. Greedy pig. Dustbin. I knew you'd be sick.

> *There is the sound of a train pulling into a station. The children stand up.* **Nick** *moves away from his sister back into the shadows.* **Carrie** *is trying to collect up the two cases and the carrier bag.*

Adult Carrie	Sent away in a train with gas masks slung over our shoulders and names written on cards round our necks. Labelled like parcels, only no address to be sent to.

> **Carrie** *is having difficulty with the luggage. She tucks the carrier bag under her arm. The* **teacher** *moves forward from the shadows. She briefly checks on what is happening.*

Teacher	Someone help Caroline.

> *The* **teacher** *moves back into the shadows.*

Adult Carrie	There was my case and Nick's and a carrier bag with a broken string handle tucked under my arm, but it kept slipping backwards and the gas mask was banging my knees.

> **Albert** *steps forward from the shadows. He is wearing an identity label around his neck and is carrying a case, a gas mask and a book. He knocks into* **Carrie**, *who drops a case.* **Albert** *picks it up.*

Carrie	Thank you.

> **Carrie** *holds out her hand for* **Albert** *to shake. He does so.*

Albert	Albert Sandwich.
Carrie	I'm Caroline Willow and this is my younger brother, Nick.

Carrie looks around and realizes that Nick has wandered off.

Carrie   Where has he got to now?

There is a pause.

Albert   Well, I suppose this is what they call our ultimate destination. Not much of a place is it?

Carrie   Bound to be dirty, a coal mining town.

Albert   I didn't mean dirt. Just that it's not big enough to have a good public library.

Carrie   (*In a cheerful and open manner*) The first place was bigger. When we stopped at the junction. Albert Sandwich? If your name had come earlier in the alphabet you could have stayed there. You only just missed it, they divided us after the Rs. Do your friends call you Ally or Bert?

Albert   (*Offended*) I don't care for my name to be abbreviated. Nor do I like being called jam, or jelly, or even peanut butter.

Carrie   I hadn't thought of sandwiches.

*The **teacher** steps forward from the shadows. She has a clipboard and list in one hand and **Nick** in the other.*

Teacher   (*To Nick*) There she is, didn't I tell you. (*To Carrie*) Carrie, don't lose him again. Two Willows, one Sandwich. In through that door with you all.

*The **teacher** ticks them off on her list and ushers them forward before returning to the shadows.*

Adult Carrie We all filed into a long, dark room with pointed windows. We were offered tea and a piece of cake and told to stand by the walls and wait for someone to choose us.

Carrie   What's happening?

Albert	A kind of cattle auction, it seems.

> **Albert** *sits down on his case and begins to read his book.*

Adult Carrie	(*Remembering how she felt at that moment*) Suppose we're not chosen? Suppose we are last, or the only ones left!
Nick	Why are people being taken away, Carrie?
Carrie	Nick, why don't you smile and look nice.

> **Nick** *looks worried.*

Carrie	(*Noticing his reaction*) It's all right, I'm not cross. I won't leave you.
Adult Carrie	Children were leaving the line and being taken away. Only the unwanted ones were left – Nick and me and Albert Sandwich, who was sitting on his case, reading a book and taking no notice. He didn't care.
Carrie	(*Putting a brave face on the situation*) Well, I don't care if we have to wait.

> **Auntie Lou** *and the* **teacher** *step forward from the shadows. They are talking.*

Auntie Lou	Two girls perhaps. Not a boy and a girl, I'm afraid. I've only the one room, see, and my brother's particular.

> **Carrie**, *in desperation, takes the initiative by walking up to Auntie Lou.*

Carrie	Nick sleeps in my room at home because he has bad dreams sometimes. I always look after him and he's no trouble at all.
Auntie Lou	Well, I don't know what my brother will say. Perhaps I can chance it. There's pretty eyes you have, girl!
Carrie	Nick's the pretty one, really.

> **Auntie Lou** *picks up the cases and carrier bag. The* **teacher** *walks over to Albert. Blackout.*

Scene 2

Auntie Lou, Carrie and *Nick* step forward from the shadows. *Auntie Lou* is carrying the cases and the carrier bag. They are outside Mr Samuel Isaac Evans's shop. *Adult Carrie* watches them.

Auntie Lou   Here we are 'Samuel Isaac Evans – Groceries'! There's a back way into the house and you'll use that, of course, but we'll go through the shop for once, as my brother's not here.

They move forward and enter the house through the shop.

Adult Carrie   The shop was dim and smelled mustily pleasant – candles, tarred kindling and spices.

Auntie Lou   (*Leading the children forward*) Now this way into the hall, and upstairs to your room.

Adult Carrie   Polished linoleum, a shining glass sea with rugs scattered like islands. Not a speck of dust anywhere.

Auntie Lou   Better change into your slippers before we go up to your bedroom.

Carrie   We haven't got any – there wasn't room to pack them in the suitcases, but...

Auntie Lou   Oh, I'm so sorry, how silly of me! Why should you? Never mind, as long as you're careful and tread on the drugget.

Auntie Lou moves to pick up the drugget and lays it out as though it were on the stairs. She then stands with the children at one end of it.

Nick   (*Whispering to Carrie*) She thinks we're poor children, too poor to have slippers.

Auntie Lou   What did you say, dear? Mr Evans doesn't like to see the drugget down. I just put it there while he's out to keep the carpet spick and span. It's new, you see. Lovely pile, and Mr Evans doesn't want it trodden on.

Nick	How are you supposed to get upstairs then? Walk on the ceiling, or fly like a bird?

Auntie Lou picks up the cases and the carrier bag and leads the children along the drugget to the top of the stairs.

Auntie Lou	Well… well of course you have to walk on it sometimes but not too often. Mr Evans said twice a day would be quite enough. You see, four of us going up and down twice a day, morning and evening, makes sixteen times altogether, and Mr Evans thinks that's quite enough traipsing. (*She indicates with her hand*) Here's the bathroom, hot and cold running water and a flush toilet.
Nick	We have to come upstairs for the bathroom!
Auntie Lou	Yes, I know, dear. But if you want to – you know – go anywhere, there's one at the end of the yard. Mr Evans doesn't use it, of course, it wouldn't be dignified for him to be seen going there, not a man in his position, when all the neighbours know he's got one indoors, but I use it, and though it's an earth closet it's quite nice and clean.
Carrie	(*Trying to stop Nick blurting out that he is used to an indoor toilet*) That will be fun, Nick, won't it? Like the one at the farm we stayed on last summer.
Nick	Spiders! There was spiders!
Auntie Lou	God's creatures! Just like you and me.
Nick	Not like me. Not like me at all! I don't have hundreds and hundreds of creepy-crawly legs and I don't eat flies for my dinner or spin sticky stuff out of my tummy! That's disgusting, spiders is disgusting, horrible and yakky.

Auntie Lou leads the two children to their bedroom in the area stage right and puts down the cases and the carrier bag.

Auntie Lou	And this is your room, just by here. It's only a small room.

Adult Carrie	Two narrow beds, a wardrobe for clothes, and one wicker chair; there was not room for more. And an embroidered picture on the wall, bearing the words...

> *Carrie* 'looks at the embroidered picture'.
> She and **Adult Carrie** speak together.

Both Carries	'The Eye of the Lord is Upon You.'
Auntie Lou	My brother is very strong chapel. You'll have to be exceptionally good. Sundays. No games or books, see? Except the Bible, of course. It may not be what you are used to but it's better to get things straight from the start, isn't it? Mr Evans is a good man, but strict. Manners, tidiness and keeping things clean. He says dirt and sloppy habits are an insult to the Lord. So you will be good won't you? You look like good children.
Carrie	We'll try to be good, Miss Evans.
Auntie Lou	And if you could remember to bring down all the things you'll want for the day in the morning.
Carrie	We'll try to remember, Miss Evans.

> *Carrie* and **Nick** take off their gas mask boxes.

Auntie Lou	Call me Auntie. Auntie Louisa, or Auntie Lou, if that's easier. But you'd best call my brother 'Mr Evans'. Mr Evans is an important man. He's at a council meeting now. I think I'd best give you supper before he comes back, hadn't I?

> *Auntie Lou* takes the children back along
> the drugget and to the area stage left. **Carrie**
> and **Nick** sit down and **Auntie Lou** 'gives
> them their supper'. She then hovers to catch
> any stray crumbs. **Adult Carrie**, who has
> been watching the scene, speaks directly to the
> audience.

Adult Carrie	It was a good supper of eggs, milk and crunchy fresh bread. Auntie Lou didn't eat but stood by the table like a waitress in a

restaurant, taking the plates to the sink as soon as they were cleared and sweeping up the crumbs round the chairs.

Auntie Lou What about bed, now? You must be very tired after your long journey. I'll just get you a candle.

> ***Auntie Lou*** *fetches a candle which she gives to **Carrie**. **Carrie** whispers to **Nick**, then together they walk along the drugget towards their bedroom, stage right. In the bedroom they start to look for their toothbrushes in their cases.*

Adult Carrie We had to be got into bed before the very important Councillor Evans came home from his meeting.

Auntie Lou (*Calling to the children*) Do be quick dears, time's getting on.

Adult Carrie There was no electric light upstairs so it was difficult to be quick holding a candle in one's hand.

Auntie Lou (*Calling again in an agitated manner*) Do be quick, dears!

Carrie Nick, just for once you'll just have to go to bed without cleaning your teeth.

Nick I won't. My mouth feels all furry and yakky.

> *There is the sound of a door being closed.*

Nick (*Anxiously*) Oh, Carrie – that must be him!

> ***Nick*** *and **Carrie** huddle together and freeze. **Auntie Lou** gets on her knees and starts to roll up the drugget.*

Auntie Lou (*In a loud whisper to the children*) Into bed now and remember to blow out the candle. Goodnight!

> ***Mr Evans*** *steps forward from the shadows looking for **Auntie Lou**. **Carrie** and **Nick** listen anxiously to the conversation between **Mr Evans** and **Auntie Lou**.*

Mr Evans	Lou! Lou! What are you up to?

Auntie Lou	Coming Samuel.

She gets up holding the drugget. **Mr Evans** *sees it in her hands.*

Mr Evans	What are you doing there? I might have known, I suppose. Up and down the stairs, soon as my back's turned, wearing out the carpet. Messing and humbugging about, up and down, back and forth, in and out.

Mr Evans and **Auntie Lou** *freeze.*

Adult Carrie	There was no light from the bedroom window because the thick blackout curtains were drawn.

Nick	(*Trying to hold back his tears*) I want Mummy. I want to go home. I don't like it here. I don't want to be safe in the country. I want Mummy and Dad.

Carrie	(*Trying to hide her anxiety*) You've got me. It won't seem so bad in the morning.

Nick	He must be an ogre, Carrie. A horrible disgusting, real life ogre.

Blackout.

. . . .

Scene 3

Lights up. **Mr Evans** *is standing in his shop centre stage. He is wearing his shop keeper's apron and is 'serving' a line of customers.* **Nick** *and* **Carrie** *are standing slightly apart watching Mr Evans.* **Adult Carrie** *stands and looks at the scene and then speaks her thoughts to the audience.*

Adult Carrie	Mr Evans. He wasn't an ogre. Just a cross man with a loud voice, pale, staring, pop-eyes and tufts of spiky hair sticking out of each nostril. Councillor Samuel Isaac Evans was a bully. He bullied his sister. He even bullied the women who came into his shop, selling them things they didn't really want to buy and refusing to stock the things that they did.
Mr Evans	(*To a customer*) Take it or leave it. Don't you know there's a war on!

*During **Adult Carrie's** speech, the customers move back into the shadows.*

Adult Carrie	He would have bullied us children if he had thought we were frightened of him. I was a little frightened, but I wasn't going to show it. Nick wasn't frightened at all. He was frightened by ogres, spiders, crabs, cold water, the dentist and dark nights, but he wasn't frightened of people.

***Nick** turns to Carrie.*

Nick	Mr Evans has false teeth that click when he talks. You can't really be scared of someone whose teeth might fall out.

***Mr Evans** removes his apron and approaches **Carrie** and **Nick**, who both stand attentively. **Auntie Lou** steps forward from the shadows. She is obviously anxious because this is the first time **Mr Evans** has had dealings with the two children. **Mr Evans** hands his apron to **Auntie Lou**.*

Mr Evans	(*To Carrie and Nick*) You've got a few manners, I see. That's something. That's a bit of sugar on the pill! You've fallen on your feet, let me tell you. You'll get good food in this house, so no fadiness, mind. No whining around my sister for titbits when my back's turned, particularly the boy. I know what boys are. Walking stomachs! I told her, 'you fetch two girls now, there's just one room', but she got round me, she said, 'the boy's only a baby'. Not too much of a 'babby', I hope. No wet beds. That I won't stand!
Nick	That's a rude thing to mention.

Mr Evans   All right, then you mind your Ps and Qs, see, and I won't
                    complain. As long as you toe the chalk line. Rules are made to
                    be kept in this house. No shouting, or running up stairs, and
                    no language. No bad language, that is. I'll have no foul mouths
                    here. I don't know how you've been brought up but this house
                    is run in the fear of the Lord.

Nick   We don't swear. Even my father doesn't swear, and he's a naval
                    officer.

Mr Evans   Oh, an officer, is he? Well, well.

Nick   A captain. Captain Peter Willow.

Mr Evans   Indeed. Then let's hope he's taught you how to behave. It'll
                    save me the trouble.

                                    Mr Evans *moves back into the shadows.*
                                    Auntie Lou *starts to follow him but does*
                                    not go out of the light.

Nick   (*Muttering*) You don't mind language, do you? I mean, I don't
                    know the deaf and dumb alphabet.

Carrie   Don't be smart, Nick.

                                    Auntie Lou *overhears what has just been*
                                    said. She smiles and then checks that Mr
                                    Evans has gone. She walks back towards the
                                    children.

Auntie Lou   Oh, his bark is worse than his bite. Though he won't stand to
                    be crossed, so don't be too cheeky and mind what he says. I've
                    always minded him – he's so much older, you see. When our
                    mam died he took me in and brought me up with his son
                    Frederick, who's away in the army just now. He treated us
                    both the same. When we were naughty he would give
                    Frederick the strap but he'd sit me on the mantelpiece over the
                    fire to make me mind my manners. I've sat there many a time,
                    scared to death of the fire and my feet pins and needles.

Nick   Our father never sat anyone on the mantelpiece or frightened
                    anyone.

Auntie Lou	Come here both of you. There's nothing for you to worry about.

Carrie and *Nick* go to her. *Auntie Lou* takes them both by the hand and they all walk off into the shadows.

Adult Carrie	Mr Evans let me work in the shop. I enjoyed that – measuring out things – giving change – I wasn't afraid of Mr Evans.

Nick steps forward from the shadows. He is carrying a biscuit jar. *Adult Carrie* watches as *Nick* unscrews the lid of the jar and takes out a biscuit which he starts to eat. *Mr Evans* steps forward from the shadows, sees what *Nick* is doing and takes him by the scruff of the neck. When *Mr Evans* starts to shout at Nick, *Carrie* runs forward from the shadows. She stands and watches the scene in growing horror.

Mr Evans	(*Shouting*) Thief! Caught red-handed now, aren't you? How long has this been going on? Sneaking in here after the shop has closed and I'm safely out of the way in the parlour? Stealing! The ingratitude of it. Oh, you'll be sorry, you'll pay. You need a sharp lesson, my lad, and I don't mind giving it. Strap's what you're asking for, isn't it? On your bare bottom!

Mr Evans unbuckles his belt, takes *Nick* and bends him over ready to beat him. *Nick* is frightened and begins to cry out. *Carrie* looks on, uncertain of what to do.

Adult Carrie	Nick had never been beaten, not even a slap. He was standing shivering. What was there to do? Fetch the police? Nick had been stealing. Auntie Lou? – but she was nowhere to be seen.

Carrie moves towards Mr Evans and Nick.

Carrie	(*Pleading*) Please, Mr Evans. Oh, please! He's only a little boy. Not a thief, just a little boy who likes biscuits. He's got a sweet tooth. He can't help it. I don't suppose he thought it was stealing.

Nick retreats from Mr Evans and his belt.
Mr Evans raises the belt and advances on Nick.

Mr Evans   Then he'll have to learn to think, won't he?

Nick   If you hit me, I'll tell. I'll go to school and tell my teacher.

Mr Evans   And what will she say, my young master? That it's a fine thing that you've done, to steal from the good people who have taken you in?

Nick   I'll say I was hungry.

Mr Evans stops in his tracks. There is a pause. Mr Evans puts the belt back round his trousers.

Mr Evans   (*To Nick*) Kneel and pray!

Nick kneels and Mr Evans stands over him. Carrie looks on disapprovingly.

Mr Evans   Oh, Lord, look down on this sinful child in his wickedness and lead him from his evil ways into righteousness…

Mr Evans continues to mouth the words of his prayer while Adult Carrie speaks.

Adult Carrie   Mr Evans prayed for half an hour or more. I'd rather have been beaten myself.

Mr Evans   Amen.

Mr Evans moves back into the shadows. Nick gets up as though nothing has happened.

Nick   I knew I could stop him if I said I was hungry. Grown-ups don't mind being nasty to children but they don't like other grown-ups to know they've been nasty.

Carrie	He's not so nasty, really. You shouldn't have pinched his biscuits, you know you shouldn't, you're not such a baby. And it was mean to say you were hungry because it's simply not true. You're just greedy for biscuits. I know he's nasty to Auntie Lou sometimes but it's her own fault because she lets him be. She's nice, Auntie Lou, but she is stupid.
Nick	It isn't her fault, he is nasty. He's mean and nasty. You know he yelled at Auntie Lou yesterday because he slipped on the mat in the hall? He said she'd polished underneath the mat, but she hadn't. I saw him. He moved the mat so that it was on a slippery bit, then sort of pretended to slip on it and then started to shout. I really and truly do hate him.
Carrie	If you really do hate it here then we ought to tell someone.

Carrie and *Nick* *freeze.*

Adult Carrie	But who could I tell? Mother and Father were far away and you couldn't exactly write about it in a letter. Our teacher said we were to go to her but what could she do? There were too many evacuees and not enough places for them to stay. How could I say to her that we wanted to leave the Evanses' house because Nick had been caught stealing biscuits?

Nick *turns to Carrie.*

Nick	I don't hate being here. I just hate him, that's all. But I don't want to leave. I'm used to it now.
Carrie	Come on Nick, and don't do anything like that again.

Nick and *Carrie* *both move off into the shadows.*

Adult Carrie	We had been there just over three weeks and yet it seemed like it was the only place we had ever lived: only slept in the bedroom with the narrow beds, only eaten in that clean kitchen, only ever used the outside earth privy in the day time, always kept out of Mr Evans's way, always been woken by the pit hooter wailing, always gone running down the hill to school.

*Adult Carrie takes a packet of letters out of
the trunk. She opens one and takes out a
photograph and the letter which she begins to
read. Mrs Willow steps forward from the
shadows to speak the words of the letter.*

Mrs Willow   Daddy's ship is on convoy duty in the North Sea and as you
can see from the address I have moved to Glasgow, then I can
see Daddy when the ship comes into port. I'm living in a small
room in a boarding house in a street near the docks.
Everything seems to smell of kippers. I did enjoy your last
letter and am very pleased to hear that you and Nick are
happy. I'm glad to hear that you both make your own beds and
tidy up after yourselves. Quite a change. Are you both
remembering to brush your teeth?

*Carrie steps forward from the shadows
holding a letter which she is reading and a
photograph. For a short while you can hear
both Mrs Willow and Carrie speaking the
words of the letter.*

Mrs Willow/Carrie   The ambulance driving I'm doing is really enjoyable and useful
but can be very tiring. I sometimes don't get to bed till after
breakfast and then I sleep through till the evening. I've enclosed
a photograph of me in uniform with my tin hat on. Smart isn't
it? Goodbye, my darlings, I can't wait to see you both.

*Carrie looks at the photograph and then
puts it and the letter into her pocket. Mrs
Willow and Carrie freeze.
Adult Carrie puts the letter and the
photograph back into the envelope. She then
takes a toy tea set from the trunk and lays it
out on a tray. Mrs Willow moves forward
and Adult Carrie offers her a cup and
saucer. She takes the cup and saucer and
moves to sit in the chair stage left. Adult
Carrie stands back to watch the events
which follow.*

Adult Carrie   And Mother did come. All the way from Scotland to see us,
for a few hours on a Saturday.

> *Carrie moves towards her mother who puts down her cup and saucer, stands, and embraces her daughter.*

Adult Carrie   It only happened the once. Now let me remember: there was me, Mr Evans, Nick, and Auntie Lou.

> *Mr Evans, Nick and Auntie Lou step forward from the shadows and freeze. Adult Carrie looks at the characters and sets the scene.*

Adult Carrie   Autumn had become winter – in the bedroom at night cold air came off the linoleum like air off an ice rink. The only warm place, the kitchen. Raw hands and feet toasted by the fire and the warmth made the chilblains itch. That's it – chilblains!

> *Nick moves towards Mrs Willow who hugs him. Mrs Willow sits down with her arms around Nick. Carrie sits at her feet. Mr Evans and Auntie Lou hover smiling. Mrs Willow takes Nick's hand and examines it.*

Mrs Willow   (*Concerned*) You've got chilblains!

Carrie   (*Defensively*) Oh, we've all got chilblains at school.

> *There is a pause.*

Adult Carrie   For a change we ate in the parlour.

> *Auntie Lou, Carrie, Nick and Mrs Willow move and stand in a table arrangement. Adult Carrie sorts them out and provides them with bits of the tea service. Mr Evans stands ready to 'pour a sherry' for Mrs Willow.*

Adult Carrie   Ugh! Slippery brown leather chairs, a harmonium in the corner, and a case of dead birds – stuffed. Mr Evans offered mother a sherry.

Mr Evans offers Mrs Willow 'a glass of sherry'.

Mrs Willow   Thank you, Mr Evans.

Adult Carrie Mr Evans didn't drink any. There was roast meat – usually only Mr Evans had that.

Mr Evans   (*To the audience*) Young people shouldn't have meat, it makes them too boisterous!

Adult Carrie Two whole slices of roast meat.

Mr Evans   (*To Mrs Willow*) They eat like troopers, you don't have to worry. Not that we have more than our ration, you know, in spite of the shop. No easy come, easy go, in this house. I was brought up in a hard school, Mrs Willow, and I don't forget it. Children today don't know they're born. Not that I've any complaints about your two, don't mistake me. I don't stand any nonsense, mind you. They do what I tell them and they speak when they're spoken to, but they know where they are with me. Don't you young Nick?

Nick looks at Mr Evans, but says nothing.

Carrie   Yes we do, Mr Evans.

Adult Carrie Then Auntie Lou said…

Auntie Lou   After the rice pudding and jam would you like a biscuit?

*Although **Auntie Lou's** offer is general she finishes up looking at Nick.*

Nick   No!

Mrs Willow   But you like biscuits, darling.

Nick   (*Forcefully*) No!

Mr Evans looks at Auntie Lou amazed that she could mention biscuits. Carrie is horrified in case Nick tells his mother about *the near beating from Mr Evans. **Auntie Lou** slowly realizes what she has said and immediately changes the subject.*

Auntie Lou   We do our best for them, Mrs Willow, we really do.

Mrs Willow   Thank you, oh, I do thank you.

Mr Evans   I think that I need to re-open the shop. There is always work to be done, Mrs Willow. Excuse me.

Mrs Willow   That was a very pleasant meal, thank you. Can I help you with the washing up, Miss Evans?

Auntie Lou   No, you stay here. The children will want to talk with you.

> ***Auntie Lou** collects the items from the toy tea service.*

Mrs Willow   But I…

Auntie Lou   (*Interrupting*) It will only take me a few minutes. I've already done most of it. You stay here and chat.

> ***Mr Evans** and **Auntie Lou** move off into the shadows leaving **Carrie**, **Nick**, and **Mrs Willow** in a family group. They move towards Carrie and Nick's bedroom, stage right. **Mrs Willow** sits on the trunk and the children sit at her feet.*

Mrs Willow   It's rather cold in your bedroom.

Carrie   Oh, we don't mind. We're not nesh!

Mrs Willow   Nesh?

Carrie   A Welsh word for feeble.

Mrs Willow   Oh, I see. I expect it's all a bit strange, all that chapel and being seen and not heard. But it's an experience, isn't it. Not like being at home of course, not so cosy, but I expect it's quite interesting. And they seem very kind in their way. Doing their best for you. (*Pause*) You are very quiet Nick?

Carrie looks anxiously at Nick. They all freeze.

Adult Carrie   There were all sorts of things Nick could have said: not being allowed in the bathroom in the day time even when it was cold; the chilblains; only having roast beef to eat when mother visited; not being allowed to eat biscuits; having to use the earth privy which had spiders and which frightened him – Nick had been constipated because of it.

Nick   Mr Evans cheats when he counts saccharine tablets.

Mrs Willow   Oh my lamb, what do you mean?

Nick   There are supposed to be a hundred in a packet. One day I recounted a packet of Mr Evans's and there were only ninety-seven.

Mrs Willow   Well, if that's the worst thing… My darlings, it's time for me to go. The train won't wait.

Mrs Willow stands up. Carrie and Nick scramble up too.

Nick   You're not going so soon are you?

Mrs Willow   It's been lovely seeing you, even for such a short time.

Nick   When are you coming to see us again?

Mrs Willow   I don't know when I can come again. The trains are so crowded with soldiers and to see you this time I had to take two days off from the ambulance station, and I can't do that again for a while.

Nick   But at Christmas?

Mrs Willow   Even at Christmas I will have to be on duty. Be good for me. It will cheer me up to know that your Christmas will be wonderful, the stars shining in the mountains and everyone singing in the Welsh way. It will be something you'll remember and treasure for the rest of your lives.

There is the sound of a steam train. **Mrs Willow** *moves away from the two children. She pauses and turns back to them.*

Mrs Willow   My darlings, you are happy here, aren't you?

Nick   Oh, I like it here very much. I don't ever want to go home again. I simply love Auntie Lou. She's the nicest person I've ever met in my whole life.

Mrs Willow moves off into the shadows. There is the sound of a steam train leaving a station. **Carrie** *and* **Nick** *wave goodbye and walk off into the shadows.*

Adult Carrie   Mother only came the once but then she, and Bongo our dog, they all belonged to another world. A world somewhere else and far away.

Blackout.

. . . .

Scene 4

Lights up. **Auntie Lou** *is standing centre stage next to* **Nick** *with her hands behind her back.* **Carrie** *is standing slightly apart from them.* **Adult Carrie** *is kneeling by the trunk, stage right. There is a shawl draped over the back of the chair, stage left.*

Adult Carrie   Just before Christmas it was Nick's birthday.

Adult Carrie takes two parcels wrapped in brown paper from the trunk and moves to hand them to **Auntie Lou**.

Auntie Lou   Happy Birthday, Nicholas.

She hands him the parcels.

Nick   Thank you, Auntie Lou.

Auntie Lou   Aren't you going to open them? (*Pointing to one of the packages*) That's from Mr Evans.

Nick tears off the wrapping paper.

Nick   (*Disappointed*) A Holy Bible!

Nick drops the Bible and the wrapping paper onto the floor and tears open the next present. *Auntie Lou* tidies up the wrappings from the floor.

Nick   Gloves! What lovely gloves, Auntie Lou! They're the best gloves I've ever had in my whole life. I'll keep them for ever and ever, even when I've grown too big for them. My tenth birthday gloves – leather with fur linings!

Nick spontaneously hugs *Auntie Lou*.

Auntie Lou   Have a happy birthday, Nick.

Auntie Lou moves away into the shadows. *Nick* puts on his gloves and admires them. *Carrie* picks up the Bible.

Carrie   The Bible's lovely too, you are lucky, Nick. It was kind of Mr Evans. I expect when he was a little boy he'd rather have had a Bible than anything else in the world, even a bicycle. So it was kind of him to think that you might feel like that, too.

Nick   But I didn't want a Bible. I'd rather have had a knife. There are some smashing knives in the shop. They're on a card by the door, on special offer. I've looked at them every day. I was hoping to get one and he knew I was. He saw me looking. He was just being mean giving me a rotten Bible.

Carrie   Perhaps he'll give you the knife for Christmas. Auntie Lou says Mr Evans is getting us goose for Christmas. That will be nice, won't it?

Nick   I'd rather have turkey!

Nick storms off into the shadows.

Carrie   (*Calling after him*) Nick, don't be silly!

She follows him into the shadows.

Adult Carrie	The goose from Druid's Bottom.

> *Auntie Lou steps forward from the shadows. She is carrying some darning. She sits down in the chair stage left and begins to sew.*

Adult Carrie It was Auntie Lou who first told us about Mr Evans's older sister – Dilys.

> *Carrie and Nick step forward from the shadows. They move to sit on the floor close to Auntie Lou. Mr Evans steps forward from the shadows but stands apart from Auntie Lou, Carrie and Nick.*

Auntie Lou (*Sewing as she talks*) The goose comes from Mr Evans's older sister. She lives out of the town and keeps poultry. Bit of an invalid she is, now. Bed-fast much of the time she is now. Poor soul, I think of her but I daren't go and see her. Mr Evans won't have it, you see.

> *Mr Evans speaks to the audience.*

Mr Evans Dilys has made her bed and turned her back on her own people, and that's that. She married the mine owner who was an Englishman. She deserves what she gets does our Mrs Gotobed!

Auntie Lou Mr Gotobed was the owner of the pit where our dad died in an accident and Dilys married into the family.

Carrie Gotobed's a funny name, isn't it?

Auntie Lou English, of course. She married him just after our dad was killed down the pit.

Mr Evans That Dilys is dancing on our father's grave! She knew that the Gotobeds were bad owners. How could she marry one of them? If they had looked after their pits our father would never have been killed by a rockfall. It should never have happened! Those Gotobeds never took any safety precautions. Too busy making money to think about the safety of their workers. Too interested in profits! All tarred with the same brush are the Gotobeds.

Auntie Lou   Now her husband's dead we should let bygones be bygones.

Mr Evans   I want nothing more to do with Dilys. She made her choice.

Auntie Lou   Dilys always makes sure we get a fine bird for Christmas.

Carrie   But if she is in bed how can she look after the geese?

Auntie Lou   Hepzibah Green rears the birds. She's good with poultry.
                      She looks after Dilys and Druid's Bottom as best she can.

Carrie   Druid's Bottom?

Auntie Lou   Bottom of Druid's Grove. Where the yew trees grow. Where
                      we picked the blackberries, up by the railway line.

Carrie   That dark place!

Auntie Lou   It's the trees make it dark. Though it's a queer place, too.
                      Full of the old religion still, people say – not a place to go
                      after dark. Not alone, anyway. I know I'd not care to, though
                      I wouldn't let Mr Evans hear me say it.

Mr Evans   Wicked foolishness. There's nothing to be afraid of on this
                      earth, not for those who trust in the Lord.

                                                Mr Evans moves back into the shadows.

Carrie   I wouldn't be afraid of the Grove. Nick might be, he's still
                      young, but I'm not scared of anything. Can Nick and I come
                      with you, Auntie Lou, when you go to fetch the goose?

Auntie Lou   Of course you can, dear.

                                                Auntie Lou, *Nick* and *Carrie* freeze.

Adult Carrie   Two days before Christmas was the time for us to collect the
                      goose, but Auntie Lou was ill. She coughed all morning and
                      her eyes were red rimmed.

                                                Carrie gets up and puts a shawl over
                                                Auntie Lou's shoulders. *Nick* stands,
                                                and together he and *Carrie* look anxiously
                                                at *Auntie Lou* as she coughs and sneezes.
                                                Mr Evans steps forward from the shadows.

Mr Evans	You're not fit to go out.
Auntie Lou	But it's Christmas in two days.
Mr Evans	You're ill and you need to get better for Christmas. Send the children to collect the goose.
Auntie Lou	I thought I'd go tomorrow. Hepzibah will know I'm not coming now, it's getting so late.
Mr Evans	Not tomorrow you can't! I want you in the shop Christmas Eve, it'll be busy. The children can go. Earn their keep for a change.
Auntie Lou	It'll be a heavy goose, Samuel.
Mr Evans	They can manage between them.
Auntie Lou	It will be dark before they get back.

Nick looks worried and Mr Evans notices.

Mr Evans	Full moon. You've not been putting ideas into their heads, I hope.
Carrie	What ideas, Mr Evans? Of course we'd love to go, we don't mind the dark.

Blackout.

. . . .

Scene 5

*Lights up. **Carrie** is standing centre stage, she has a large bag in her hands. **Nick** is standing some distance from her. They are walking* down to Druid's Bottom. **Adult Carrie** looks on, clearly visible. The area stage right is set as the library at Druid's Bottom, with piles of books and possibly a bookcase.*

Carrie	What is there to be scared of? Just a few old trees. All that queer place stuff is just Auntie Lou being superstitious. You know how superstitious she is. I'm not surprised Mr Evans gets cross with her sometimes. She's so scared, she'd jump at her own shadow. There's the path down through the trees...

Nick	You go. I'll wait here.

Nick stops and looks around apprehensively but Carrie continues walking.

Carrie	Don't be silly! Don't you want a mince pie? We might get a mince pie. It's not far. Auntie Lou said it wasn't far down the hill. Not much more than five minutes.
Nick	You go!

The gap between Carrie and Nick widens.

Carrie	(*Coldly*) All right, have it your own way. But it'll be dark soon and you'll be really scared then. Much more scared by yourself than you would be with me. Druids and ghosts coming to get you. Wild animals too. Wolves! But I don't care. Even if I hear them howling and snapping their jaws I shan't hurry back.
Nick	(*Wailing*) Carrie, wait for me, wait! Don't leave me Carrie!

Nick runs forward and holds onto Carrie.

Carrie	(*Jokingly*) I thought it was you leaving me.

Nick tries to laugh but it turns into a sob. There is a sound like that of deep breathing.

Carrie	Do be quiet, Nick!
Nick	Why?
Carrie	I don't know.

Carrie and Nick freeze.

Adult Carrie	Something... something here, something waiting. Deep in the trees or deep in the earth. Not a ghost – nothing so simple. Something old and huge and nameless.
Nick	Carrie...
Carrie	Listen!

Nick	What for?
Carrie	Shhh!

The two children freeze listening.

Adult Carrie	It was as if the earth were turning in its sleep. Or a huge nameless thing were breathing.

The breathing stops.

Carrie	Did you hear?

***Nick** cannot reply for his tears.*

Carrie	It's gone now. It wasn't anything.

There is the sound of someone running and shouting – it is indistinct and like a gobbling sound.

Nick	Yes there is! There it is now!
Carrie	Run! Don't look back whatever you do!

***Carrie** and **Nick** run in panic*.*

Adult Carrie	Running, stumbling, slipping, sliding. The gobbling thing following. Calling out after us.
Carrie	(*In panic*) Don't look back, Nick, whatever you do!
Nick	I can't run any more, I can't Carrie…
Carrie	Yes you can! Not much further!

***Carrie** takes **Nick's** hand to make him run faster.*

Adult Carrie	The path widened and flattened as it came out of the Grove. I caught hold of Nick's hand to make him run faster. Too fast for his short legs and he fell on his knees.
Nick	I can't Carrie!

Nick falls on his knees.

Carrie   Get up Nick! Quickly! Run!

Adult Carrie   The house! Its dark tall chimneys loomed up and there were lights in the windows. Running across the dirt yard towards the light. There was a door but it was shut.

Nick   The thing is still coming after us, Carrie!

> *Carrie reaches the 'door' and 'knocks' on it, crying out.*

Carrie   Please open the door before it's too late!

Adult Carrie   The door opened like magic and there was…

> *Hepzibah Green and Albert step forward from the shadows into the area, stage left, as the children fall backwards into the kitchen at Druid's Bottom.*

Hepzibah   Hepzibah Green.

Carrie   Shut the door, please. Miss Evans sent us for the goose but something chased us. We ran but it chased us. Sort of gobbling. Oh please shut the door or it'll come in!

Hepzibah   Bless you, love, it's only Mister Johnny. I didn't know he was out.

Albert   He went to shut up the chickens. I expect he went for a walk after.

Carrie   It wasn't a person. It didn't talk, it went gobble-gobble.

Albert   That's Mister Johnny's way of talking. It could frighten someone. Though I expect you frightened him just as much.

Hepzibah   (*Calling out of the 'door' quietly*) It's all right, Mister Johnny, all right.

Hepzibah, Albert, Carrie, and Nick freeze. Adult Carrie puts a jacket on a tailor's dummy which becomes Mister Johnny and moves it close to Hepzibah. As she does this she speaks and moves so that she is standing near Carrie.

Adult Carrie   Someone appeared in the doorway – stood close to Hepzibah, as if for protection. A small person with a shy crumpled up face. He tried to smile but he couldn't smile properly because one side of his face seemed dragged down. He made a sound in his throat – spitting as he spoke. Chuckle, gobble – I couldn't move.

Hepzibah   Mister Johnny, say how-do-you-do to our visitors will you?

Nick confidently walks up and 'shakes hands' with Mister Johnny.

Nick   Hello, Mister Johnny. I'm Nick. Nicholas Peter Willow and I'm just ten. It was my birthday last week. And Carrie, my sister, will be twelve next May.

Hepzibah realizes that Carrie is afraid of Mister Johnny.

Hepzibah   Albert, while I see to Mister Johnny you take Carrie to fetch and pack the goose.

Hepzibah, Nick and Adult Carrie with Mister Johnny move off into the shadows. Albert fetches a wrapped packet representing the goose and he and Carrie put it into the bag she has been carrying. They put the bag down on the floor. Adult Carrie moves to stand in the half-light.

Carrie   (*To Albert*) I thought Mr Gotobed was dead. Mr Evans's sister's husband.

Albert   That's not him. Mister Johnny is a sort of distant cousin of that Mr Gotobed. He used to live in Norfolk but when his parents died he came here with Hepzibah. She's been his nurse since he was born. Bit of a shock, I suppose, first time.

Carrie	Is he mad?
Albert	No more than a lot of people. Just a bit simpler than some. Innocent, is what Hepzibah calls him. She's a witch.
Carrie	A witch?
Albert	Oh, not what you're thinking of. No black cats and broomsticks, just what country people call a wise woman. When I was ill with pneumonia, rheumatic fever…
Carrie	(*Interrupting*) So that's why you weren't at school. You were ill. I did wonder where you were.
Albert	…Hepzibah made some herbs into medicine for me and I got better quite quickly. The doctor was amazed – he had thought I was going to die. And to think I was only put here because I told the billeting officer that I liked books. Otherwise I'd be pushing up the daisies. There is a library in this house. A proper library. Shall I show you?

Albert and *Carrie* *move across to the area stage right.*

Adult Carrie	Books – shelves and shelves of books, reaching to the ceiling, most of them bound in pale calf with gold lettering on their spines.
Albert	Here we are. Marvellous isn't it? And to think nobody uses it – only me!
Carrie	Where's Mrs Gotobed?
Albert	Gone to bed. She's dying, I think. She's been ill for ages. I read to her sometimes when she isn't too tired. Do you like reading?
Carrie	Not much.
Albert	What do you do then? When you're not at school, I mean?
Carrie	I help in Mr Evans's shop sometimes. Nick's not allowed to but I am. And I play on the mountain and slide down the slag heap.

Albert	Oh! If you don't care for books perhaps you'd like to see the screaming skull. There's an interesting story about it. Untrue, I dare say, but interesting all the same.
Carrie	It sounds horrible.
Albert	It's only a skull. Come and see.

> *Albert* moves across the stage and *Carrie* follows him. He picks up a box containing a skull and opens its lid. *Carrie* peers inside.

Adult Carrie	Inside the box, resting on velvet was a small skull. Pearly smooth and grinning.

Albert	Touch it.

> *Carrie* gingerly touches the skull.

Carrie	What's the story?

> *Hepzibah* and *Nick* step forward from the shadows and overhear what *Albert* says.

Albert	Ask Hepzibah, she tells it better than I would. It's supposed to be the skull of an African boy brought here during the slave trade, but it's a load of old nonsense of course.
Hepzibah	I'll give you nonsense, my lad! Mister Albert Uppity-Know-All. You don't know so much yet, or, you'd know that wise people don't mock what they don't understand.
Albert	I'm sorry, Hepzibah. Please tell the story to Carrie.

Hepzibah takes the box and moves over to the kitchen, stage left. Albert, Carrie, and Nick follow her. She sits down on the chair with the children sitting around her. As she tells the story she takes the skull out of the box and uses it to emphasize and dramatize her words.

Hepzibah The African boy was brought here when he was ten or so. It was the fashion at that time for rich people to have a little black page, dressed up in silks and satins. So they fetched this poor innocent away from his family, across the sea, to a strange land. And of course he cried, as any child might cry, taken from his mother.

Carrie Little boys do get homesick.

Albert It wasn't a little boy!

Albert leans over to point out on the skull the things he describes.

Albert The skull has sixteen teeth in the top jaw, which means it has wisdom teeth too. And you don't get wisdom teeth until you are eighteen.

Hepzibah Albert! I thought you wanted me to tell the story.

Carrie Please carry on.

Hepzibah Well, the Gotobeds weren't hard people. The young ladies gave him sweets, toys and made a real pet of him, but they couldn't comfort him, and in the end they said he could go back home one day.

Nick Carrie and me will be going back home one day.

Hepzibah Of course you will.

Carrie Nick! Listen to the story.

Hepzibah Perhaps they meant it, but he died of a fever the first winter here and it must have seemed to him that they'd broken their promise. So he put a curse on the house. He said, on his death bed, that they could bury his body but when his flesh had rotted they must dig up his skull and keep it in the house or some dreadful disaster would come. The walls would crumble. And they believed him, people believed in curses then, and they did what he said. The skull has been kept in the library ever since.

Carrie   (*Interrupting*) And would something terrible happen if the skull was taken out of the house?

Hepzibah   It has been taken from the house just once, when old Mr Gotobed's grandmother was a girl. She couldn't abide the thought of the skull just sitting there grinning. It gave her bad dreams she said, so she took it one morning and hid it in the stable loft.

Carrie   What happened?

Hepzibah   Nothing happened at all. She waited all day to see and then went to bed, no doubt very pleased with herself. But in the middle of the night there was a loud scream like a screech owl and a loud crashing sound. And when the family came running down, all the crockery was smashed in the kitchen, all the glass in the dining room, every mirror in the house cracked to pieces. Then the girl said what she had done and they fetched the skull back and had no trouble after. It must never leave the house again otherwise who knows what will happen! There!

Hepzibah stands up holding the skull.

Nick   Thank you for the story. Mr Evans doesn't tell us any…

Carrie   (*Interrupting*) Nick! Mr Evans is too busy to tell you stories.

Albert   It can't be a true story. Can I have the skull Hepzibah? (*She hands it to him*) Thank you. Now, see those wiggly lines at the top? That's the sutures, where the bones are starting to join up. So it must have been a grown person's skull. But it's too small and light for an adult male, so it must have been a woman.

Albert puts the skull back into the box.

Carrie   It's a lovely story, Albert, don't you dare spoil it. We ought to be going, really. Auntie Lou knew we might stay for a while but it's getting late now and she'll start to worry.

Albert   I'll come with you if you like, as far as the railway.

Hepzibah   Mister Johnny will see them safe through the Grove. You'll be all right with him. No harm of the kind you are afraid of ever comes near the innocent.

Carrie   Mr Evans says no harm can ever come to those who trust the Lord.

Hepzibah   Perhaps that's another way of saying the same thing. Come again, love. Both of you, whenever you like. (*She calls towards the shadows*) Are you ready Mister Johnny to walk the children through the Grove?

Carrie   (*To Hepzibah*) Goodbye and thank you. Bye Albert.

                      Carrie *picks up the bag containing
                      the goose.*

Albert   See you both.

                      Hepzibah *and* **Albert** *waving move off
                      into the shadows.* **Adult Carrie** *carries
                      Mister Johnny forward and* **Nick** *moves
                      to stand with the tailor's dummy.* **Carrie**
                      stands staring at the two of them. **Nick**
                      'talks' to Mister Johnny.

Adult Carrie   Mister Johnny talked in his gobbly voice all the way back but then Nick started too, as though answering.

Nick   (*To Carrie*) Don't look straight at him, like that. It upsets him when people stare at him. Goodbye Mister Johnny.

                      Nick *joins Carrie.* **Adult Carrie** *moves
                      Mister Johnny into the shadows.*

Carrie   He was trying to say goodbye wasn't he? You didn't understand anything else he said, did you? Not really? I mean, I couldn't.

Nick	Only because you weren't listening.
Carrie	All right, then. What did he say? Come on, since you think you are so clever.
Nick	He said a lot of things. He said we must come back again and he'd show us his cow and where the gulls nest up on the mountain. He said he liked us though he liked me best.
Carrie	Liar! You're making it up. What a mean, dirty trick! Now help me with this goose.

> *Carrie* and *Nick* carry the goose between them.

Nick	Carrie, I want to be at Druid's Bottom all the time. I don't want to go back to the Evanses', I really don't. I never did want to be there but it's worse now, not better. I want to go home.
Carrie	Then as Mr Evans says, 'Want must be your master, Nicholas Peter Willow'.

> *Blackout.*

· ·

Scene 6

Lights up. **Mr Evans** *is sitting in the chair stage left writing in a notebook. He is doing his accounts.* **Adult Carrie** *is watching him.*

Adult Carrie	With Mr Evans you couldn't let him know that you liked someone or that you had enjoyed anything. I could tell he got jealous.

> *Carrie* and *Nick* step forward from the shadows. They are carrying the bag containing the goose.

Mr Evans	(*Without looking up*) Did you see my sister? House in good order? Get a good tea?
Carrie	She was in bed. The house and the tea were all right.

Nick   Carrie, it was a lovely house and a lovely tea Hepzibah gave us.

Mr Evans   (*Looking up from his notebook*) Better than you get here, I
                     suppose? Oh, it's all right when you don't foot the bill, isn't it.
                     That Miss Hepzibah Green. She'll not stint anyone, I dare say,
                     but then it doesn't come out of her pocket. She doesn't have to
                     sweat and slave for every penny.

                                    Auntie Lou *steps forward from the shadows.*
                                    *She realizes that **Mr Evans** is angry. To*
                                    ease the tension, she moves over to the
                                    *children and together she and **Nick** take the*
                                    goose out of the bag.

Auntie Lou   Hepzibah's a good housekeeper, Samuel. She's been good to
                     poor Dilys.

Mr Evans   And why shouldn't she be? She's on to a good thing and she
                     knows it. A mistress too ill to keep her eye on the books.
                     Feather her own nest if she chooses, and no one to know.

Carrie   I thought Hepzibah Green was quite nice. But the house is
                     very old, big and dark. We were a bit scared by Mister Johnny.

Mr Evans   So you saw the idiot did you?

Nick   (*Distressed*) Mister Johnny's not an idiot, he's not! I think you
                     are just…

                                    Nick *starts to cry.*

Carrie   (*Putting her arm round Nick to comfort him*) It's been such a
                     long walk for Nick, he's tired and ought to go to bed.

                                    Carrie *moves **Nick** away from Mr Evans*
                                    *towards their bedroom, stage right. **Auntie***
                                    ***Lou** and **Mr Evans** freeze. In the bedroom*
                                    ***Nick**, frustrated by what has taken place, is*
                                    angry with Carrie.

Nick   I think you're the meanest thing on this earth, Carrie Willow. A
                     mean, ugly cow. Saying Hepzibah was 'quite nice' in that voice.

Carrie   I didn't mean…

Nick	(*Interrupting*) You are a traitor, that's what. You're worse than he is. Leave me alone. I hate him and I hate you and I won't listen!

> **Nick** *covers his ears with his hands and sits down with his back to Carrie.*

Carrie	It's not fair. You're not fair.

> **Carrie** *leaves Nick and starts to return towards Mr Evans and Auntie Lou but stops when she overhears* **Mr Evans** *talking.*

Mr Evans	The girl's got her head screwed on all right. Miss Green didn't take her in, did she, with her soft smarmy ways? I tell you Lou, it might be a good idea to get her to go there sometimes, keep her eyes open. I know what I think Miss Green's up to, but I'd like to be sure.
Auntie Lou	You want the child to spy?
Mr Evans	Spying! What sort of word is that, girl? Am I the sort of man to set a child spying? Keep her eyes open, that's all I said. No harm in that, is it? It's Dilys I'm thinking of and you should have thought of her, too. She's our own flesh and blood whatever she's done.
Auntie Lou	That's the first time I've heard you say it Samuel. For a good many long years.
Mr Evans	Oh, I don't forgive her, that's one thing. And it was one thing, see, when she had her pride and her strength. But that's gone from her now, isn't it? And it hurts me to think of her, helpless in that woman's power.
Adult Carrie	I wanted to tell him straight that I did like Hepzibah. That he had it all wrong.

> **Carrie** *starts to walk towards Mr Evans.*

Mr Evans	(*Noticing Carrie*) What are you doing, girl? You went to bed didn't you? Up and down, up and down, tramp, tramp, tramp on the carpet.

Carrie	I walked on the paint.
Mr Evans	Go back to bed!

Blackout.

· ·

Scene 7

Lights up. The area stage left is now Mrs Gotobed's bedroom. **Mrs Gotobed** *sits in a chair, wearing a ballgown, hidden from the audience by a screen.* **Adult Carrie** *takes a tin out of the trunk stage right and puts it down. She then opens the diary and reads aloud.*

Adult Carrie   December the twenty-fifth. Christmas presents from the Evanses – a Bible for me and a blunt penknife for Nick. December the twenty-sixth, twenty-seventh. It has turned cold and started to snow, great cotton wool flakes, falling from a dark sky. The twenty-ninth of December woke up to clear sunshine and a white dazzling world.

> **Mr Evans** *steps forward from the shadows and picks up the tin. He moves to the area centre stage and calls into the shadows to Carrie.*

Mr Evans   Carrie!

> **Carrie** *steps forward from the shadows.*

Mr Evans   Lovely day for a walk, eh Carrie?

Carrie   Yes it is, Mr Evans.

Mr Evans   Tell you what. Run along to Druid's Bottom and take Miss Green this tin of biscuits. (*He hands the tin to* **Carrie**) A little present, see, to say thank you for the goose.

Carrie   (*Surprised*) Yes, Mr Evans.

Mr Evans   Good; and keep your eyes open, eh?

> **Mr Evans** *moves back into the shadows.*

Carrie	Why should he want to send Hepzibah biscuits? Spying, is it?

> *Carrie moves back into the shadows. Hepzibah steps forward from the shadows. She is carrying a candle. She moves to Mrs Gotobed's bedroom, stage left, puts down the candle and folds back the screen to reveal Mrs Gotobed.*

Adult Carrie	Somewhere upstairs in the house at Druid's Bottom someone was crying. Not as though they were in pain but very quietly and evenly, as if out of some dreadful despair. It was the saddest sound I had ever heard.

> *Carrie steps forward from the shadows carrying a tin of biscuits. The sound of someone crying can be heard clearly. Carrie pauses centre stage and stands listening to the crying with a worried expression on her face. Hepzibah picks up the candle and moves from Mrs Gotobed's side towards Carrie.*

Adult Carrie	When Hepzibah appeared at the top of the stairs I felt ashamed of listening.
Hepzibah	Oh, it's you Carrie.
Adult Carrie	Hepzibah's voice was pitched low and soft. A spell-binding voice. The voice of a beautiful witch holding the lighted candle in the darkness.

> *Mr Evans steps forward from the shadows away from Mrs Gotobed and Hepzibah but where Carrie can see him.*

Mr Evans	My own flesh and blood, my poor sister, helpless in that woman's power.
Adult Carrie	It was Mrs Gotobed crying.

> *Mr Evans moves back into the shadows.*

Hepzibah	Carrie love, don't be frightened. It's only…

Carrie   (*Interrupting*) I'm not frightened. Mr Evans sent you this tin of
                     biscuits.

                                     *Carrie gives **Hepzibah** the tin of biscuits.*

Hepzibah   That's very nice of Mr Evans. Lemon creams are Mister
                     Johnny's favourites. If you'd like to, you can go and keep Mrs
                     Gotobed company, while I make us all some tea.

Carrie   Thank you, I'd like to.

                                     Hepzibah *moves off into the shadows.*
                                     Carrie *walks towards Mrs Gotobed and
                                     then hesitates as though uncertain of what
                                     she will find.*

Mrs Gotobed   Come in. Pretty child. Sit by me. (***Carrie*** *sits on the floor*)
                     Let me look at your eyes. Albert says they are like emeralds.

Carrie   Oh.

Mrs Gotobed   Hepzibah thinks that looks don't matter but they do, you
                     know. Do you like my dress?

Carrie   It's lovely.

Mrs Gotobed   My husband gave it to me
                     just after we were married.
                     My waist was small; they said
                     they had never seen anyone
                     with such a small waist. Mr
                     Gotobed could hold it in his
                     two hands. He bought me
                     twenty-nine ball gowns, one
                     for each year of our marriage
                     and I have them all still,
                     hanging in my closet.
                     I put on a different one
                     each time I get up.
                     I want to wear each one
                     of them one more time
                     before I die.

Adult Carrie	I thought she was mad. Sitting there in a beautiful dress.
Mrs Gotobed	I'll tell you about my dresses. I've got a green chiffon with pearls sewn round the neck and a blue brocade and a grey silk with pink ostrich feathers. That was my husband's favourite so I'm keeping that one till last. I looked like a queen in it he always said.
Adult Carrie	Her eyes were pale grey and bulged a little. They were like Mr Evans's eyes but sitting there, in her finery, she did not look like a shopkeeper's sister.
Mrs Gotobed	So you're my brother's evacuee, God help you.
Carrie	I like Mr Evans.
Mrs Gotobed	Then you are the only one who does. Cold, hard, mean man, my brother. How do you get on with my baby sister?
Carrie	Auntie Lou's nice.
Mrs Gotobed	Nice, but a fool. She should have left him a long time ago. She'll lie down and let him walk over her till the end of her days. Does he walk over you?
Carrie	No, not at all.
Mrs Gotobed	Not afraid of him? Well, if you're not, then you can tell him something from me. When I die, you can tell him from me, that I hadn't forgotten him. That I hadn't forgotten he was my own flesh and blood, but that sometimes you owe more to strangers. Tell him that I've done what I've done because it seemed right to me, not because I wanted to spite him. Do you understand what I've told you?
Carrie	Yes.
Mrs Gotobed	Only wait till I'm safely dead first. Or he'll be round here, stamping and yelling and I haven't the strength for it.

Mrs Gotobed slumps back in her chair. Jumping up Carrie moves away from Mrs Gotobed and calls out in a worried voice.

Carrie	Hepzibah! It's Mrs Gotobed, something has happened to her!

> *Hepzibah hurries forward from the shadows. Carrie is staring at the body of Mrs Gotobed. She is transfixed. The sound of Mrs Gotobed's breathing is heard.*

Hepzibah	It's all right, she's just gone to sleep.

> *Blackout.*

· ·

Scene 8

*Lights up. **Adult Carrie** is kneeling by the trunk stage right reading from her diary.*

Adult Carrie　　On my birthday in May Mr Evans and Auntie Lou gave me handkerchiefs and Mother sent me a green dress that was too small for me. Auntie Lou said she could sew a piece of material on the bottom for me. After school Nick and I went to Druid's Bottom. Hepzibah had cooked a cake with white icing and twelve candles and Mister Johnny made me a crown of wild flowers. I was the Queen of the May.

> *Mr Evans steps forward from the shadows. He is waiting impatiently. There is the sound of excited children's voices. Mr Evans sits in the chair, stage left. He looks displeased. Carrie and Nick step forward from the shadows. They are clearly happy.*

Mr Evans	Oh, it's you then?
Carrie	Who did you think it was, the cat's mother?
Mr Evans	Whatever has got into you, girl?
Carrie	Nothing, Mr Evans, just nice things, that's all.
Mr Evans	Taken your time haven't you? Other people in the world beside yourself, you know. Waiting for their tea.

Carrie	I told Auntie Lou we were going to see Hepzibah straight after school. We're not late.
Mr Evans	Oh no, not at all. (*He stands up*) Come and go as it suits you. Liberty Hall, that's what you've made of my home. Your birthday tea's ready but you were having a better time somewhere else! Oh, don't trouble to answer. It's written all over you.
Carrie	I said we'd be back by half past six, and we are.
Mr Evans	Oh, ordering your meals now, is it? Servants at your beck and call, that's our place! And no gratitude – your auntie can slave for you, work her fingers to the bone, but it's Miss Green gets the thank yous. And what for, may I ask? Easy enough to keep open house when someone else pays, isn't it? Miss Green can ask in what riff-raff she chooses. Everyone welcome and no bills presented.
Carrie	It's only me and Nick who ever go there.
Mr Evans	Have you been invited though? My sister's house, isn't it? She ever invite you? That doesn't worry you, I suppose, since you've never seen her.
Nick	Carrie has seen Mrs Gotobed, so there!
Carrie	(*Hurriedly*) Only just the once.
Mr Evans	And why didn't you tell me?

> **Mr Evans** *takes* **Carrie** *by the arm and holds her.*

Carrie	I didn't think.
Mr Evans	(*Shaking* **Carrie**) Didn't think! Didn't think what! I'm not supposed to be interested, is it? My own flesh and blood and I'm not interested to hear of her?
Carrie	There wasn't anything to say.
Mr Evans	She said nothing, did she? Sat dumb? No message for me, for her brother? Come on, don't lie to me, girl.

Auntie Lou bustles forward from the shadows. She is wearing a new blouse and lipstick. She deliberately draws attention to herself.

Auntie Lou   Look Nicholas!

Nick   That's a new blouse, Auntie Lou.

Mr Evans is outraged by the appearance of his sister and turns his anger on her.

Mr Evans   A frivolous women is an abomination in the sight of the Lord.

Auntie Lou   (*Deliberately ignoring Mr Evans*) Do you like my blouse, Nick? It's the one my friend gave me when I went to stay with her. She gave me lipstick, too.

Mr Evans   Lipstick!

Auntie Lou   Most girls wear lipstick, Samuel. I didn't want to be different when we went to the dance.

Mr Evans   Dance?

Auntie Lou   At the camp. The American base, down the valley.

Mr Evans   American soldiers. (*To Carrie and Nick*) Out of here, both of you. I have a few things to say to my sister.

Mr Evans drives Carrie and Nick away. They go to their bedroom stage right and 'listen intently' to the voice of Mr Evans 'shouting' at his sister. Mr Evans makes angry gestures and rubs the lipstick from Auntie Lou's mouth. They freeze.

Carrie   Auntie Lou must be stark mad to come in and let him see her like that. She knows what he's like!

Nick   She only did it to take him off you. To stop him bullying you on your birthday.

Carrie   Oh. (*Pause*) How long will he go on, d'you think?

Nick	Just till she cries. Then he'll make her wash her face and we can have tea. You hungry, Carrie?
Carrie	No.
Nick	I'm not either. I couldn't swallow. Getting used to things doesn't make them any better, does it? What did he want you to tell him?
Carrie	I don't know.
Nick	You do. I could tell by your face that you did. So could he, I expect.
Carrie	He wants me to tell him something about Hepzibah. Like she's cruel to his sister. But that's only part of it. I won't spy for him! I won't! I won't tell him anything!
Nick	You don't have to, do you? He can't make you.
Carrie	I don't know.

Blackout.

. . . .

Scene 9

*Lights up. **Adult Carrie** is sitting in the chair, stage left. Her eyes are closed. There is the sound of someone knocking on a door. **Carrie** and **Nick** step forward from the shadows. Simultaneously, **Carrie** moves towards the 'door' which she 'opens' and **Nick** moves to stand slightly apart from her. **Major Harper**, an American soldier, steps forward from the shadows.*

Major Harper	Major Harper, ma'am. Major Cass Harper. Is Miss Louisa Evans at home?
Carrie	There's just me and Nick here at the moment.
Major Harper	Then may I come in and wait till Miss Louisa comes home?
Carrie	Oh, no, you can't do that, I'm afraid. Mr Evans might come back first, you see.
Major Harper	Miss Louisa's brother? Why, I'd be glad to get acquainted with him.

Carrie	He might not be glad though. He doesn't – he doesn't like American soldiers. (*Realizing what she has said*) It's nothing personal. I mean, I'm sure you're awfully nice, it's not that.
Major Harper	I'm a very respectable American soldier.
Carrie	There's no point in your staying, really there isn't. It wouldn't be any good at all. Even if you did see her, Mr Evans wouldn't let you go out with her, to a dance or the pictures, or anything. Mr Evans says dance halls and cinemas are the haunts of the Devil and a frivolous woman is an abomination in the eyes of the Lord.
Major Harper	Miss Louisa is a lovely, gracious lady and I wouldn't wish to be a trouble to her.
Carrie	You would be, I'm afraid. He'd make her cry. He's always making her cry.
Major Harper	I see. I'm obliged to you for explaining the situation. Perhaps you'll say… (*Pause*) tell her I called. Just that. And that I'm real sorry I missed her.

> ***Major Harper*** *moves back into the* shadows. ***Carrie*** *turns as though shutting a door in relief.* ***Nick*** *moves to her.*

Nick	(*Shouting*) You rotten, mean pig. That's her friend come to see her and you sent him away!
Carrie	I couldn't ask him in, could I? Suppose Mr Evans came back?
Nick	Mr Evans, Mr Evans. All you think about is Mr Evans. What about poor Auntie Lou?
Carrie	There'd be an argument and she'd cry. I can't bear it when she cries.
Nick	You can't bear it! What's that got to do with her? Maybe she'd rather see her friend first even if she had to cry after. I'm going to tell her.

> ***Nick*** *runs quickly away into the shadows.*

Carrie	(*Calling after Nick*) Wait for me! She's in the chapel. We'll tell her.

> *Carrie follows **Nick** into the shadows. **Adult Carrie** opens her eyes and rises from the chair.*

Adult Carrie	Mr Evans. Hepzibah always said that Mr Evans had a cold hard life. He had seen his own father die down the pit and hadn't been able to save him. Mr Evans had a lonely life and it made him bitter against those who had it too easy.

> *Mr Evans steps forward from the shadows. He is carrying his accounts notebook. He sits in the chair stage left and works. **Adult Carrie** watches him.*

Adult Carrie	We found Auntie Lou scrubbing the floor in the chapel and we told her that her friend had come. Nick and I finished cleaning the chapel. As we walked back home there was no sign of Auntie Lou, the American, or his jeep.

> *Carrie steps forward from the shadows. She moves towards Mr Evans.*

Mr Evans	Where's your auntie?
Carrie	After she finished at the chapel, as it was such a lovely evening, she went for a walk up the mountain.
Mr Evans	Figures, figures. There's no end to it. No peace for the righteous.
Carrie	Must you work so hard?
Mr Evans	Sympathy is it? That's something I don't ever get. No help for it is there, with this old war going on? Can't even get a boy to deliver! But the only things worth having are the things you've worked hard for, and I'll last out. Don't you worry. Go and have your supper.

> *Carrie lingers as **Mr Evans** goes back to his accounts. He freezes. **Carrie** moves to stand quite close to Adult Carrie. **Carrie** speaks to the audience.*

| Carrie | I've lied! I can't tell him about Auntie Lou and her American friend. Suppose she comes back and tells him she's been somewhere else? He'll never trust me again if he finds out the truth. I had to lie! It is all so complicated! |

Blackout.

. . . .

Scene 10

Lights up. **Adult Carrie** *is sitting in the chair stage left reading from her diary. A tea chest is in position centre stage to represent a broken stone wall.*

| Adult Carrie | It was in July that Mrs Gotobed died. After school on the day it happened, Hepzibah sent Albert to Mr Evans with a note. Mrs Gotobed had died in the morning but there has been no way of letting Mr Evans know earlier in the day. After he had read the note Mr Evans went round the shop and pulled down the blinds. 'Respect for the dead' he said. Albert and I went for a walk. We went up the mountain and sat on a broken down stone wall. |

Carrie and Albert step forward from the shadows. They sit down on the tea chest.

| Carrie | She's the first person I've ever known die in my life. |

| Albert | She won't be the last so you might as well get used to it. |

| Carrie | (*Sharply*) Do you have to speak like that? |

| Albert | No! But it was the way you spoke! (*Imitating Carrie's self-pitying tone*) 'This is the first sorrow of my life, poor little me.' |

| Carrie | I didn't mean that. |

| Albert | Didn't you? |

| Carrie | No I didn't. |

There is a pause.

| Albert | I'm sorry if I was unkind. |

Carrie	It's all right.
Albert	No, I'm upset and taking it out on you.
Carrie	It doesn't matter. (*Pause*) Did she – I mean, did it hurt her much? Dying?
Albert	Hepzibah said it was just like putting a light out at the end of the day.
Carrie	What'll happen to Hepzibah? Will she have to leave Druid's Bottom? I mean she's just the servant, she can't stay there, can she? Where will she go? And what'll happen to Mister Johnny?
Albert	Hang on Tragedy Queen, it's all right. Mrs Gotobed told me it would be a sin if they were turned out when she died. She said she was going to make a will saying they could both stay on, without paying rent, as long as they wanted to. I think she's left her bits of jewellery to your Auntie Lou – there's not as much as you'd think, mostly glittery junk, paste copies of real stones. And the house goes to Mr Evans, though it won't be much use to him. He can't sell it or let it of course, while Hepzibah is living there.
Carrie	'Her own flesh and blood. But sometimes you owe more to strangers.'
Albert	What's that about?
Carrie	It's what she told me to tell Mr Evans when she was dead. That what she's done – made this will – not to spite him but because it seemed the right thing. And the right thing was to take care of Mister Johnny and Hepzibah. I didn't understand what she meant when she said it to me.
Albert	You just thought she was mad.
Carrie	But I understand it now. Mr Evans will be so happy to know that everything is going to be all right and that in spite of their arguments deep down his sister still loved him.
Albert	I wouldn't be too sure about him being happy.
Carrie	He'll weep for joy when I tell him.

Albert	I wouldn't be in too much of a hurry to tell him, if I were you.

> *Albert moves off into the shadows. Carrie freezes. Mr Evans steps forward from the shadows into the area stage left. Carrie goes to him. Adult Carrie gets up from the chair and moves to another part of the stage. As Adult Carrie speaks to the audience, Carrie's lips move as she 'speaks' to Mr Evans.*

Adult Carrie   I rushed home to tell Mr Evans the good news, because good news can never wait. I told him what Mrs Gotobed had told me. I used the exact words that she had and then I explained what she had meant by them.

> *Mr Evans barges past Carrie and starts shouting to Auntie Lou who is out of sight in the shadows. Carrie is dumbfounded.*

Mr Evans   I knew it! I knew it! Louisa, Louisa! I told you what was going on! I told you she'd got her claws in, but you wouldn't have it. Miss Green this. Miss Green that. So kind to poor Dilys. She knew what she was doing, the viper. Doing me out of my rights and fixed up a snug home for herself for the rest of her days! But I shan't let it lie! Not if I have to drag her through every court in the land. Well, Carrie I'm much obliged to you. Out of the mouths of babes and sucklings!

> *Mr Evans storms off into the shadows. Carrie bursts into tears.*

Carrie   (*Through her tears*) I don't understand. I only told him so that he would be pleased. Perhaps I didn't explain it properly. I told him how I'd feel. I only tried to put myself in his place. I was sorry for him and thought he'd be pleased. Something dreadful is going to happen and it will be my fault. I must find a way of warning Hepzibah.

> *Carrie dashes into the shadows.*

Adult Carrie   I hadn't meant any harm. I just passed on a message but it was like innocently opening the lid of a box and letting out a dark shapeless shadow.

*Albert and **Hepzibah** step forward from
the shadows. **Albert** is carrying some school
books and **Hepzibah** is holding a mixing
bowl. They move to the area stage left which
becomes the kitchen at Druid's Bottom.*

Adult Carrie   After school I ran all the way to Druid's Bottom but the dark
shadow stayed with me. I could not escape from it. When I
ran, it ran too.

*Carrie runs out of the shadows. She is
breathless. She moves towards Albert and
Hepzibah. There is a pause. **Albert** looks
up from his books. When he speaks, his voice
is disapproving.*

Albert   We've had a visitor!

Hepzibah   Only natural that Mr Evans should want to come to Druid's
Bottom and pay his last respects to his sister.

Albert   Poke around in her things that's what he came to do.

Hepzibah   Her next of kin, Albert. Within his rights there.

Albert   (*Bitterly*) And to tell you to clear out Hepzibah? Was that
within his rights, too?

Hepzibah   A month's notice is reasonable. Gives me time to find
somewhere. It shouldn't be difficult, there's plenty of farms
could do with a bit of help with men away at the war. We only
want two rooms and our keep and I've got a strong back and
I'm willing. So's Mister Johnny in his own way. He's good with
cows and sheep, lambing time.

Carrie   But Albert! You said Hepzibah and Mister Johnny could stay
in the house. That the will said so!

Albert   I was wrong, it seems…

Carrie   But you told me…

Albert   And you told Mr Evans, didn't you!

Carrie   When I spoke to Mr Evans about the will he wasn't pleased
                    and I thought he would be. He just got angry and started
                    shouting at Auntie Lou. I don't understand.

Albert   You shouldn't have told Mr Evans anything, stupid!

Hepzibah   That's enough, Albert! There's no will and that's that! Mr
                    Evans rang the bank and Mrs Gotobed's London solicitors
                    and there is no sign of a will anywhere. She had a kind thought
                    and she believed that she'd carried it through and that's not
                    uncommon with someone as sick as she was and in pain a lot
                    of the time. So there's no call for you to blame her.

Albert   (*Pointedly*) I don't blame Mrs Gotobed.

Hepzibah   Now you two make friends. I've to get on with cooking tea no
                    matter what and I expect to see you the best of friends by the
                    time this has cooked or you'll get the sharp side of my tongue.
                    I'm short on patience this evening. Do you hear me?

                                    Hepzibah *moves off into the shadows.*
                                    There is a pause.

Carrie   I'm sorry, Albert.

Albert   It's Hepzibah and Mister Johnny you should be sorry for!

                                    There is another pause. ***Albert*** *closes his*
                                    book and holds his hand out to Carrie.

Albert   Come on, we must do as Hepzibah asked.

                                    Carrie *shakes hands with* ***Albert***.

Albert   There may be some hope yet, so I want to show you
                    something.

                                    They move to a different part of the stage.

Albert   Your Mr Evans. He came up here and he went through all her
                    dresses, counted them and wrote down the number. Then he
                    told Hepzibah that he'd hold her responsible. As if he thought
                    she might steal them!

Albert moves to pick up an ornate box.

Carrie	Is it Mrs Gotobed's jewellery box?
Albert	He was in here making his lists and writing everything down.

Albert opens the box and lifts out a tray. He looks disappointed.

Albert	Oh, well. There was just a chance, I suppose.
Carrie	Chance of what?
Albert	When Mr Evans was in here he must have taken the brown envelope that Mrs Gotobed always kept under this tray.
Carrie	A brown envelope?
Albert	He found it and took it. That's it! The will was in the brown envelope!
Carrie	You saw him take it?
Albert	Don't be silly! He wouldn't let me see something like that, would he?
Carrie	No, I suppose not. So how do you know?
Albert	Once when I helped Mrs Gotobed to put on her pearls the envelope was there. I didn't think too much about it, why should I? Then when Hepzibah said that there wasn't a will I remembered the envelope I'd seen in there. The will must have been in the envelope and Mr Evans found it and he's taken it.
Carrie	Mr Evans wouldn't just take Mrs Gotobed's will! Why should he do that?

Albert

God give me strength. Carrie, you innocent nit! If a person dies without making a will – everything they've got to leave goes to the nearest relative. Mr Evans and Auntie Lou in this case. The house will go to them, the jewels and the dresses. Nothing to Hepzibah, not even the right to stay on here. So all Mr Evans had to do was take the will and destroy it.

Carrie

But that would be terribly wrong.

Albert

Clever girl.

Carrie

I don't believe he would do such a thing. If you believe he did, tell someone.

Albert

Oh yes? Who'd listen to me? To a fourteen-year-old boy who thinks he once saw an envelope in a jewellery box. If only I'd looked last night. If only you hadn't had to shout your mouth off about the will and brought that foul man roaring around the place.

Carrie

That's not fair!

Albert

Fairness doesn't come into it. What happens to Hepzibah is important. She's been crying. She'll say it's all right, that she'll manage, but how can she?

Carrie

Suppose – suppose she asked Mr Evans to let them stay, at least for a while – till the war's over?

Albert

She's too proud to do such a thing. Besides it wouldn't do any good, would it?

Hepzibah

(*Calling the children from the shadows*) Come on you two, it's time to eat. Come on before it gets cold.

> **Albert** *moves off into the shadows.* **Carrie** *lingers.*

Albert

(*As he moves out of sight*) Come on, Carrie.

> **Carrie** *freezes.*

Adult Carrie	Mr Evans was honest. No one was ever short changed in the shop. Once, when I didn't give Mrs Pritchard the right amount, Mr Evans worked it out and made me take sixpence back to her.

Carrie moves forward and talks to the audience.

Carrie	Stealing a will would be very wicked. Mr Evans believes in the Lord and rules and good behaviour. Yet Albert seems so sure that a will was made and kept in a brown envelope in Mrs Gotobed's jewellery box. Someone must have the will. But who has got it? Mr Evans? No! It's so unfair. Mr Evans *is* unfair. Poor Hepzibah and Mister Johnny.
Albert	(*Calling from the shadows*) Come on Carrie!

Carrie moves off into the shadows.

Adult Carrie	Mr Evans could be kind. He let old age pensioners have credit if they were short at the end of the week, and once sent a box of free groceries to a poor woman whose husband had died of pneumonia. 'It's the Lord's will we should take care of widows and orphans' that's what he had said. It is the Lord's will to help but he believed that Hepzibah had bewitched Mrs Gotobed. Hepzibah? I wasn't sure about her being a witch. She was good at most things, making pastry, telling stories and keeping poultry so if she was good at magic she could have used it to keep the house.

Mrs Willow steps forward from the shadows and stands isolated.

Mrs Willow	My dearest Carrie and Nicholas, I have left the ambulance unit because Granny is ill. I've also rented a house up here so that I can look after her and still be close to the docks when Daddy's ship comes in. It's more like a cottage than a house, but it has an attic room for you both so we can be together again. There's a good school not far away. I'm sure we'll all be very happy in our new home and we'll all be near Daddy.

Carrie steps forward from the shadows reading a letter. For a short while we hear Carrie and Mrs Willow reading together.

Carrie/Mrs Willow   I have written to Auntie Lou sending the money for your train ticket and all the information. See you in a few days my darlings.

> **Mrs Willow** *stops reading and moves back into the shadows. There is a pause.*

Carrie   Love from Mother.

> *There is another pause.*

Carrie   I have to do something now. Just a few days. I could ask Mr Evans if Hepzibah and Mister Johnny can stay in the house. I've just got to choose the right moment.

> *Blackout.*

· ·

Scene 11

Lights up. **Mr Evans, Auntie Lou, Carrie,** *and* **Nick** *are sitting centre stage on a rug 'having a picnic'.* **Adult Carrie** *watches them.*

Mr Evans   (*To Carrie*) I'm going to miss my assistant. You've been a real help to me, Carrie. Our last picnic together then. Used to come up here quite a lot when I was a lad. Seems to have got steeper though. Used to carry your auntie up here when I was a young man and she was a babby. Do you remember that Lou?

> **Auntie Lou** *smiles and 'looks out over the valley'.*

Adult Carrie   Auntie Lou was oddly quiet, she seemed in an odd mood altogether, though not a sad one. She sat looking out over the valley with a dreamy look in her eyes and a small secret smile on her face.

Mr Evans   (*Standing up*) Time we were on our way back. Some of us have to work for our living.

Nick   Thank you for the picnic, Mr Evans.

Mr Evans	You might as well have these now, mightn't you. I've got a council meeting tonight. You'll be fast asleep when I get back.

> *Mr Evans takes two packets from his pocket giving one each to Carrie and Nick. The children open their presents, Nick hurriedly but Carrie more carefully. Nick holds up a sheath knife.*

Nick	I've always wanted a real sheath knife. I mean the penknife you gave me for Christmas was very nice but it doesn't cut things. This is just what I wanted, it's my very best thing.
Mr Evans	Take good care of it then.
Carrie	(*Holding up her present*) A gold ring...
Mr Evans	Real gold.
Carrie	A real gold ring with a small dark red stone. It's beautiful!
Mr Evans	As long as you're pleased. Just a keepsake to remember us by. From your auntie too, mind.
Carrie	Thank you so much Auntie Lou.
Mr Evans	Well, there's work to be done.

> *Mr Evans moves off into the shadows. Carrie stands and calls after Mr Evans.*

Carrie	Thank you Mr Evans. The present is lovely.

> *Nick and Auntie Lou sit close together. They are laughing and seem to be sharing a secret.*

Auntie Lou	Best tidy everything away, then.

> *Auntie Lou moves to pack away the remains of the picnic, and fold up the rug. Nick stands up.*

Carrie	(*Whispering to Nick*) What were you and Auntie Lou talking about?
Nick	It's a secret. You're Mr Evans's friend. Helping him all the time. I'm Auntie Lou's! (*To Auntie Lou*) Let me help you clear up, Auntie Lou.

> **Nick** *starts to help Auntie Lou. She looks at him and holds her arms open to hug him and then* **Carrie**.

Auntie Lou	Oh, there's happy I've been with you two, there's been life in the house, first time I've known it!

> *Blackout.*

· ·

Scene 12

> *Lights up.* **Adult Carrie** *is sitting in the chair stage left. She speaks to the audience.*

Adult Carrie	There was to be a farewell tea at Druid's Bottom. In the afternoon Mister Johnny was playing with the skull of the African boy.

> **Hepzibah**, **Nick** and **Albert** *step forward from the shadows.*

Hepzibah ·	(*Shouting in the direction of the shadows*) Put that down, Mister Johnny. This minute! Oh, it doesn't matter, I suppose, not the old skull, but he's running me ragged just lately, picking things up and putting them down where they shouldn't be. He had the silver this morning – all the best spoons, out in the yard.
Albert	You'd just polished them and it was the shine that attracted him, you know he's like a magpie that way. He was only making patterns with the spoons, you've never minded before.
Hepzibah	Things are different now, aren't they? I don't want Mr Evans finding anything missing.
Albert	He'd hardly make a fuss about an old skull. I'll get the skull from him.

Nick	No, I'll go. You have to be careful when you ask Mister Johnny for things. He can get very stubborn.
Albert	All right then.

> As **Nick** *walks into the shadows we can hear him speaking to Mister Johnny.* **Carrie** *steps forward from the shadows and joins Hepzibah and Albert. She has the ring that Mr Evans gave her in her pocket.*

Nick	(*In the shadows*) Look what I've got Mister Johnny. My new knife. It's sharp as a razor, a real hunting knife, but if you keep the sheath on you can hold it a bit.
Carrie	(*To Hepzibah and Albert*) Nick doesn't want to leave here. He'll miss it all.
Hepzibah	We'll all be pulling up sticks about the same time. I'd better see to tea. It's all ready so don't hang around out here for too long you two.

> **Hepzibah** *moves off into the shadows.*

Albert	I'm being sent to live with Mr Morgan, the minister, so I'll still be living in the valley.
Carrie	All the poultry, that's Hepzibah's isn't it? And the cow belongs to Mister Johnny. What'll happen to them?
Albert	They'll be sold, I suppose. It all depends on what turns up. Beggars can't be choosers. You shouldn't be able to turn people out of places they've lived in for years. It doesn't make sense. There should be a law about it. If she made a will someone would know, some solicitor or someone. It's no use because I haven't enough proof – even you don't believe me.
Carrie	That's mean, Albert Sandwich.
Albert	I know it is and it's just because I'm too scared to do anything. I want to put things right but I'm too scared. I hate myself!
Hepzibah	(*Calling from the shadows*) Nick, Carrie, Albert, tea's ready!

Albert	(*Calling back*) Coming Hepzibah!

> **Nick** *runs out of the shadows towards Albert and Carrie. He is carrying the skull.*

Nick	Albert, I've got the skull from Mister Johnny.

> **Carrie** *takes the skull.*

Carrie	I'll put this back in the box in the library.
Albert	Well done Nick.
Nick	It wasn't difficult. I let him stroke the leather on my sheath knife and he gave it to me. My new knife is a really brilliant knife. Look. Mr Evans gave it to me and he gave a ring to Carrie. Do you want Carrie to show her new ring to you? Tea's ready! Come on! (*Calling off*) Mister Johnny!

> **Nick** *runs off into the shadows.* **Hepzibah** *steps forward from the shadows. They pass each other.*

Hepzibah	(*To Nick's departing figure*) That's it Nick, go and get Mister Johnny.

> **Hepzibah** *walks up to Albert and Carrie.* **Carrie** *takes the ring out of her pocket.*

Carrie	(*Showing Albert the ring*) Mr Evans gave it to me. (*To Hepzibah*) Mr Evans gave it to me, Hepzibah.

Albert	It's Mrs Gotobed's ring isn't it. It's her garnet ring. The ring she wore most of the time. He stole it! He stole it! And what else did he steal? What else did he take out of that box?

Hepzibah   All right, Albert. Even if it did belong to Mrs Gotobed it belongs to Mr Evans now, doesn't it? You cannot steal what's your own! I'm glad that Mr Evans gave it to you. Mrs Gotobed would be glad too, if she knew. So don't you pay any heed to Albert's old nonsense.

Albert   It's not nonsense. He took it without telling anyone and he shouldn't have done that until the estate is settled. That's the law, Hepzibah! And if he took the ring he might have taken something else, mightn't he?

Hepzibah   Albert, that's enough! Tea!

Carrie   Just let me put the skull back in its box in the library.

Hepzibah   Thank you Carrie. Now come on Albert and no more. We're going to enjoy our farewell tea and afterwards I'll tell you a story.

> **Hepzibah** and **Albert** *begin to walk into the shadows.*

Carrie   (*Talking to herself*) Mr Evans did steal the will. He did. He doesn't care about anyone else. Not Hepzibah, not Mister Johnny. He doesn't care. I'll show him. He won't have Druid's Bottom. I'll take the skull and throw it into the pond in the yard. No one will find it and the curse on the house will come true.

> **Carrie** *walks towards the shadows and pauses in the half-light.*

Albert   (*Voice only from the shadows*) Mrs Gotobed made a will and Mr Evans stole it.

Hepzibah   (*Voice only from the shadows*) The African boy put a curse on the house if his skull ever left it.

Albert   (*Voice only from the shadows*) If Mr Evans can steal a ring then he can steal a will.

Hepzibah   (*Voice only from the shadows*) The house has stood safe because the skull is kept inside.

Albert	(*Voice only from the shadows*) Mr Evans is a mean, greedy man who will throw Hepzibah and Mister Johnny out of the house.
Carrie	He won't have the house! He won't! I won't let him!

> **Carrie** *throws the skull into the shadows.*

Carrie	Sink! Sink in the pond! Let the African boy's curse come true!

> *Blackout.*

• •

Scene 13

Lights up. **Adult Carrie** *is standing by the trunk stage right. She speaks to the audience.*

Adult Carrie	Albert came looking for me. He found me by the pond. I was just standing there. He told me that Hepzibah had found a place. A farmer wanted a housekeeper and she could take Mister Johnny. A hill farm, a bit bleak. I was so tired but I was sure that Albert had no idea what I had done with the skull. We promised to write to each other like true friends should. But I never did. I don't know why. Then he didn't write to me either. It was all so complicated.

> **Carrie** *and* **Nick** *run on from the shadows.*

Carrie	We're late! I hope Auntie Lou won't be angry.
Nick	(*Laughing*) Oh no, she won't be angry.
Carrie	I don't see what's so funny!
Nick	Honestly Carrie, I don't think Auntie Lou will be worried that we are late.

> **Carrie** *takes hold of* **Nick's** *arm. She wants to know the truth.*

Carrie	Nick, what do you know? I've noticed recently you and Auntie Lou have been as thick as thieves, whispering and giggling together.
Nick	She won't be there.

Carrie	What do you mean? Why won't she be there?
Nick	I suppose it's safe to tell, now.
Carrie	Tell what?
Nick	Auntie Lou has gone. Gone with Major Cass Harper. They're getting married tomorrow.
Carrie	You knew! Nicholas Willow! Why didn't you tell me?
Nick	You might have told Mr Evans.
Carrie	Oh, Nick. Did she think so? Was that why she told you and not me?
Nick	She didn't really tell me, it was just that I guessed and I plagued her to find out. She told me to keep it in the dark, not meaning that you couldn't know, but I thought – well, you know what you are. Sorry for Mr Evans all the time.
Carrie	I'm not sorry for him now!
Nick	We should get home quickly and go to bed before he comes home from his meeting and finds Auntie Lou gone.

> *Carrie* and **Nick** *run back into the shadows.* **Adult Carrie** *watches them go and then moves across the stage to pick up a case. She carries the case to the bedroom area stage right and starts to 'pack it'. As she does this* **Mr Evans** *walks slowly out of the shadows and slumps into the chair, stage left.*

Adult Carrie	Mr Evans. I had been sorry for him but he cheated me. He gave me a ring that didn't belong to him; a ring he had stolen as he had stolen Mister Johnny's safety and happiness when he had stolen the will.

> *Carrie steps forward from the shadows. She approaches Mr Evans.*

Mr Evans	(*Looking up*) Bit early isn't it?

Carrie	Late you mean, don't you? It's half past five.
Mr Evans	I was just going to wake you. Train goes at seven.
Carrie	You been up all night?

Mr Evans nods.

Mr Evans	Cup of tea, bit of breakfast. Bacon, I thought. Fried bread and tomatoes. Something hot to set you up for the journey.
Carrie	Yes, but not for Nick. The grease might upset him. He gets sick on trains.
Mr Evans	Porridge then?
Carrie	I can do that.

Mr Evans gets up.

Carrie	Auntie Lou…?
Mr Evans	Gone off with her fancy man. Did you know?
Carrie	The truth is Nick did. I didn't.
Mr Evans	She's made her own bed. Much good may it do her.
Carrie	Are you angry?
Mr Evans	Ate a lot your Auntie Lou did. Always at it, munch, munch, nibble, nibble, just like a rabbit. Now she's gone there will be one less mouth to feed. (*Pause*) Told the boy did she? Why couldn't she tell me, then? Face to face, instead of stealing away like a thief in the night! Just leaving a note! That does rile me a bit.
Carrie	Perhaps she was scared of what you might say?
Mr Evans	Scared? What's she got to be scared of me for? No – to make me look small, that's her object. Just like her fine sister Dilys. The two of them make a right pair, sending messages, leaving notes – you look at this now.

	*Mr Evans takes a brown envelope from his pocket. **Carrie**, who is amazed, watches as he takes from it an old photograph.*
Mr Evans	An old photograph. That's all I had from Dilys on her death bed – and not even sent to me, neither! I had to find it in an old envelope, going through her things and making a record as her grand London lawyer instructed me.
Carrie	(*Looking at the photograph*) Is that – is that you and Mrs Gotobed, then?
Mr Evans	(*Nodding*) I'd be ten years about. Dilys a bit older. Forty-five years ago. A long time you'd be thinking. Only other picture of her I keep in my watch.
	Mr Evans puts the first photograph back in the envelope and returns it to his pocket. He then takes out his pocket watch and opens its cover.
Mr Evans	Here see! (*Carrie looks at the second photograph*) See the ring that she's got on? That's the one you've got now. I bought it for her see, with my first wages, and when she gave it back, I gave it to you. So there's a bit of history you've got with that ring.
Carrie	(*Swallowing hard*) When she gave it back?
Mr Evans	Don't parrot, girl! You heard me! It was with the picture. No letter, nothing – just my name on the envelope tucked away in her jewel box.
Carrie	In a brown envelope in her jewel box. (*Pause*) Nothing else at all?
Mr Evans	What else should there be?
	*Mr Evans puts away his pocket watch and the second photograph. There is a pause. **Carrie** smiles.*
Mr Evans	What are you grinning for?

| **Carrie** | I'm just glad. I'm glad she sent them back, the ring and the picture. It meant she remembered, didn't it, that she thought of you? |

Mr Evans   Seemed more like a slap in the face to me. But take it your way, if you like. Now get upstairs double quick and wake up that idle young brother of yours, or you'll be missing your train.

Carrie   Yes, I'll get him

Mr Evans   And make sure that you've both packed all your things.

> *Carrie* walks towards the bedroom area
> stage right. She picks up the case which
> *Adult Carrie* has been packing. *Nick* steps
> forward from the shadows carrying a case.
> *Carrie*, *Nick*, and *Mr Evans* move into
> the area centre stage which now becomes the
> railway station. *Mr Evans* stands
> awkwardly. *Nick* is impatient for the train
> to arrive. The sound of a train pulling in at
> a station is heard.

Adult Carrie Mr Evans had come with us to the station. He made certain that we got a seat in a carriage.

> *Nick* sits on his suitcase as if it were a
> carriage seat.

Mr Evans   You'll be all right now. No point in my waiting.

> *Mr Evans* ruffles *Nick's* hair.

Mr Evans   Young Nicodemus.

> *Mr Evans* touches *Carrie's* cheek.

Mr Evans   And Carrie.

Adult Carrie He just turned on his heels and walked away from us.

> *Mr Evans* walks off into the shadows.
> *Adult Carrie* moves to the chair stage left
> and sits down.

Carrie	(*Calling after him*) Goodbye, Mr Evans.

> *There is the sound of a guard's whistle and the noise of a train slowly pulling away from the platform.* **Carrie** *puts down her case next to Nick's and sits on it. We hear the sound of the train building up speed.*

Nick	That's over then.
Carrie	Don't be mean. He was quite nice in the end.
Nick	Nice?
Carrie	Not bad then. I wonder if Albert'll be waving up on the line. I would if I was him.
Nick	At this time in the morning! We can wave to the house, though. There's a place where you can see it, after the bend.
Carrie	I shan't look. I don't think I can bear to.
Nick	When can we open our lunch packet, Carrie? My stomach is flapping!
Carrie	Not yet.

> **Carrie** *closes her eyes and pretends to sleep.* **Nick** *stands up as though at the carriage window.*

Nick	Goodbye town, goodbye war memorial, goodbye chapel on Sundays, goodbye slag heap, goodbye mountains, goodbye trees. Goodbye Druid's…

> **Carrie** *jumps up and pushes* **Nick** *down onto his case, holding him there.*

Carrie	Sit down Nick!
Nick	Let go of me, rotten beast! Let go, I want to see Druid's Bottom!

Carrie lets go of Nick and turns to the
'window'. The train whistles. **Nick** is also
trying to see out of the 'window'.

Nick   (*Shouting*) Goodbye Druid's Bottom!

Carrie screams. **Nick** looks in horror at
Carrie. He turns and walks off into the
shadows.

Carrie   (*Sobbing and calling out*) It's on fire, Nick! Druid's Bottom's
on fire. Blazing away, flames and smoke – they'll be dead.
The flames! They'll all be dead! And it's all my fault… Nick!

Carrie stands alone. **Adult Carrie** is still
sitting in her chair.

Adult Carrie   I'll never forget. I can't forget.

Carrie   It was my fault. I threw away the skull and the curse did
the rest.

Adult Carrie   No Carrie, that wasn't how it happened.

Carrie   Everything must have been destroyed.

Adult Carrie   Most of the house was but you didn't cause the fire.

Carrie   I took the skull and threw it into the pond.

Adult Carrie   But they are not all dead, they weren't killed by the fire.
What happened wasn't your fault. Remember Hepzibah and
what she said. Just listen to Hepzibah, she knows the truth.

> *Hepzibah steps forward from the shadows into the half-light.*

Hepzibah   Carrie always used to believe my old stories.

Carrie   I'll never forget.

Adult Carrie   Memories are like those old stories of Hepzibah's – they can't be forgotten.

Carrie   But the fire?

Hepzibah   The house was gutted. Mister Johnny playing with matches.

Adult Carrie   So everything is all right.

> *Albert steps forward from the shadows into the half-light.*

Albert   You didn't write to me and you promised.

Carrie   But you were all dead.

Adult Carrie   You never wrote either, Albert. If you had, I might have known sooner that everyone was safe.

Hepzibah   Mr Head and Miss Heart – both stubborn as mules when their minds were fixed.

Adult Carrie   (*Agreeing*) Yes.

Carrie   It was the curse of the African boy. I know it was. I wanted Hepzibah and Mister Johnny to live in the house at Druid's Bottom. That was what Mrs Gotobed wanted and Mr Evans would have sent them away. That's why I took the skull.

Adult Carrie   But Mr Evans didn't steal the will. There wasn't one.

Carrie   There was a fire! I saw it!

Adult Carrie   There is no need to worry, Carrie. No one at Druid's Bottom was hurt. Not Hepzibah, Mister Johnny or Albert Sandwich.

Hepzibah   Only Mr Evans has died since the fire.

Adult Carrie   And he probably died of loneliness.

Albert   (*Calling*) Carrie!

Carrie   Yes, Albert.

Adult Carrie   (*Echoing*) Albert.

Albert   We are all well. Hepzibah still looks after Mister Johnny. He's been having speech therapy to help him make himself understood when he speaks. He's getting on fine.

Hepzibah   (*Calling*) Carrie!

Carrie   Yes, Hepzibah.

Adult Carrie   (*Echoing*) Hepzibah.

Hepzibah   Auntie Lou. You remember she married Major Cass Harper?

                     *There is a slight pause as both **Carries**
                     remember and nod in agreement.*

Hepzibah   Well, her son sold Druid's Bottom to Albert Sandwich. He's repaired the place and one day he is going to come and live here. Everything is all right now.

                     *There is a pause as **Hepzibah** and **Albert**
                     move back into the shadows. Both **Carries**
                     watch them go.*

Carrie   I'll never forget, even when I'm grown up!

Adult Carrie   Memories are like that. But everything and everyone is all right. You don't have to worry.

                     ***Carrie** begins to move towards the shadows.*

Adult Carrie   Goodbye Carrie.

Carrie   (*From the shadows*) Goodbye.

Activities

What the Adapter Says

This adaptation of **Carrie's War** had a life before it was published in the Playscripts series. The starting point was the need to find appropriate material to make into a play to take into schools. The original version toured schools and gave over 130 performances. Since then, it has gone through many changes from the initial drafts and first performances to this version which you can read and perform for yourselves.

Watching the play was not intended to be a substitute for reading the book, and it was hoped that the production for schools would encourage the students to go away and read the novel for themselves. If they had already read it, they would then be able to compare the play with the novel, which could lead to some thought-provoking class discussions.

An adaptation for stage cannot last as long as it takes to read the original novel, but it should not be seen as just a 'shorter' version. It should have something of value to offer in its own right. This adaptation does not copy the structure of the novel; instead it focuses on Carrie as an adult, as she recalls her memories of her time as an evacuee in Wales, remembering the people she knew then, and sharing her feelings about them and the things that happened during that time. In this way, she can provide the playscript with a narrative and recreate some of the descriptive passages found in the novel.

The original cast was made up of four actors, which meant that each actor had to play more than one rôle. The actor playing Adult Carrie also took the part of Carrie as a young girl. To do this, she did not change her clothes, but sometimes wore a scarf or a label, and used her voice and her body to show the difference between the two characters. The other actors put on specific articles of clothing when changing characters: for example, a bowler hat and a waistcoat for Mr Evans; a school cap for Nick; a pair of glasses for Albert. Some scenes called for more than four characters on stage at one time, like when Mrs Willow comes for tea at the Evanses'. On this occasion, the actor playing Adult Carrie took two dolls from her trunk to represent young Carrie and Auntie Lou. The decision was made to use a tailor's dummy to represent Mister Johnny. In the novel, Mister Johnny is important because of the effect he has on other people in the story. It did not seem appropriate for an actor to represent him in the playscript because he only appears a couple of times and it would be difficult to communicate the vulnerability of his character convincingly; also because everything he says is translated through someone else.

This sort of production does not reproduce the kind of 'real' world created by a novel, film, or television adaptation. Instead, it asks its audience to enter into a non-naturalistic world and allow itself to believe (like a child) that a cardboard box can represent a fort, a car, a wall or anything else and one actor can 'become' a number of very different characters.

This published playscript is different in a number of ways to the original production which toured the schools. It has scene breaks and more stage directions. Each character on the cast list can be played by a different person (unless you choose to double-up, or use dolls or puppets). This provides more individual acting roles and so allows a greater number of people to take part. However, for the reasons I have already explained, I made the decision to keep the tailor's dummy for Mister Johnny (see A Note on the Set, page 5). The simplicity of the set and the almost bare acting area help keep the action flowing as it did in the original production and remain true to the 'non-naturalistic world' described on page 78.

Carrie's War is an intriguing story and offers a valuable insight into the years of the Second World War and particularly daily life in the rural areas which had changed little since Victorian times. Through the voice of Mr Evans we hear the attitudes of many people of the time to children and close relatives and the moral codes by which they lived their lives. In his shop and house, we see a world where domestic chores were demanding, particularly during the cold weather and without the benefits of electricity and gas. All these things and more – the roles of men and women, the lack of choice of leisure time entertainment – show how much the world has changed in the last 50 years, and in particular, highlight the social and cultural framework within which many people today grew up.

Robert Staunton

The Need for Evacuation

During the First World War (1914-1918), aeroplanes and giant air balloons called Zeppelins were used by the Germans to drop bombs on England. In over a hundred such air raids, 14,000 civilians died. The threat of war grew again in the 1930s. The rise of Adolf Hitler and his Nazi party in Germany threatened the peace which had existed since 1918. Hitler wanted to win back the respect and power that his country had lost and to make it great again.

Aeroplane technology had come a long way since the First World War and the British government knew that if there was to be another war, lots of people were going to die in air raids. So they began to make plans to evacuate people from Britain's major cities as soon as war broke out.

Read

Making Plans
Britain was divided into three areas:
Evacuation areas: towns and cities which could be targets for German bombers.
Reception areas: country towns and villages where people would be safe.
Neutral areas: no one left these areas and no evacuees were sent there.

The evacuation areas included:
- London
- The Medway towns of Chatham, Gillingham, and Rochester
- Portsmouth, Gosport, and Southampton
- Birmingham
- Liverpool, Bootle, and Birkenhead
- Manchester and Salford
- Sheffield, Leeds, Bradford, and Hull
- Newcastle and Gateshead
- Edinburgh, Rosyth, Glasgow, Clydebank, and Dundee

Talk and Write

1 In small groups, look at a map of Britain.
2 Why do you think these cities and towns were chosen as evacuation areas?
You may want to consider these issues:
- the importance of naval ports
- where the majority of the population lived
- what the essential wartime industries were
- where these industries were located.
3 Make a list of your reasons and share them with the rest of the class.

Preparing for Evacuation

Read

Gas

Poison gas had been used as a weapon in the First World War. The government believed that the Germans would drop gas from aeroplanes over Britain. Over 40 million gas masks were issued and people were encouraged to carry them around at all times. (As it happened, no gas was dropped and many people stopped carrying their masks.)

It was decided that all children over the age of five, pregnant women, mothers with children under the age of five, and disabled people would be evacuated. It was not a legal requirement for people to be evacuated, but all parents were encouraged to send their children out of the danger areas.

Design

Design a poster aimed at persuading parents to send their children away to safe areas. The poster should appeal to the parents' sense of responsibility and emphasize the importance of keeping children out of harm's way. The poster could also remind parents that if their children were safely cared for in the country, then mothers would be available to 'do their bit' for the war effort. In the play, when Carrie and Nick are evacuated, their mother, Mrs Willow, becomes an ambulance driver.

Read

Packing a Bag

During the summer months of 1939, there were many rehearsals for evacuation. Children packed their bags and practised the evacuation procedure. Each child had a name label and carried their personal possessions in a suitcase or a bag. The list below was given to some London schoolchildren, suggesting what they should take.

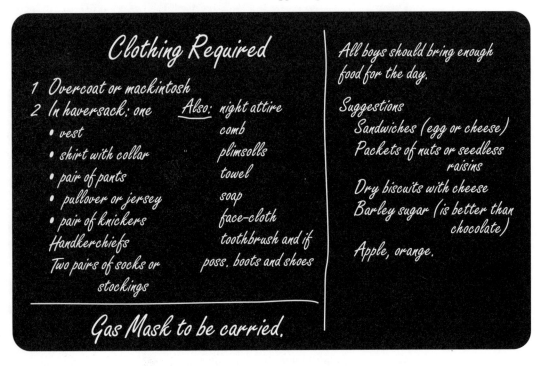

Clothing Required

1 Overcoat or mackintosh
2 In haversack: one *Also:* night attire
 • vest   comb
 • shirt with collar plimsolls
 • pair of pants   towel
 • pullover or jersey soap
 • pair of knickers face-cloth
 Handkerchiefs   toothbrush and if
 Two pairs of socks or poss. boots and shoes
    stockings

All boys should bring enough food for the day.

Suggestions
 Sandwiches (egg or cheese)
 Packets of nuts or seedless raisins
 Dry biscuits with cheese
 Barley sugar (is better than chocolate)
 Apple, orange.

Gas Mask to be carried.

'We weren't told where we were going. Just told to turn up at our schools, with a packed lunch and a change of clothes...'

Carrie

Discuss

1 How do you think Carrie and Nick felt, having to leave their personal possessions behind?
2 How would you feel if you were going away and all you could take was a change of clothes?
3 Which of your clothes would you take?
4 What possessions would you miss the most? Why?

Write

1 Imagine you are going to be evacuated today. You are only allowed to take one suitcase with you. Make a list of the things you would take. Remember, you have to be able to carry the suitcase!
2 If you had to choose only *one* personal possession to take with you, what would it be? Write down your reasons for your choice.

The Moment Arrives

Read

As the likelihood of war increased during the summer of 1939, many people began moving away from the cities. On 1 September 1939, the Germans invaded Poland. On the same day, the evacuation of Britain's children began in earnest. Teachers and helpers were also evacuated. They helped to organize the children onto the trains and buses that took them out of the cities into the countryside. No one knew exactly where they would end up, not even the teachers.

Millions of children said goodbye to their mothers and fathers, not knowing when they would meet up again. By the end of September 1939, over three and a half million people had been evacuated from the cities.

Read and Write

The Journey

1 Look back at Scene 1 and re-read pages 8-9 – Carrie and Nick's train journey to Wales.

2 Imagine you are Carrie. Write down the thoughts you have as you travel on the train to your unknown destination. You could think about what she might feel about the following things:
- leaving home
- leaving family and friends
- looking after Nick
- looking ahead to the future.

Read

Cattle Market

Carrie   What's happening?
Albert   A kind of cattle auction, it seems.

When the evacuees arrived in the countryside they had to wait to be chosen by foster parents. They usually had to wait in school and church halls whilst local people came along and made their choice of whom they would take. Billeting officers were responsible for finding 'billets' (temporary homes) for all the children, mothers and teachers.

Foster parents were paid ten shillings and sixpence (about 53p) for looking after one evacuee and eight shillings and sixpence (about 43p) for each additional child. Some evacuees had kind people looking after them, but there are lots of stories of children being badly treated, locked up, and even beaten by their foster parents.

Write

1 Imagine you are a billeting officer. Write a speech to give to the local villagers, trying to persuade them to take one or two young evacuees into their homes. Try to appeal to people's sense of duty to the war effort. You may also wish to include the fact that they will receive money for their trouble!

2 Read the speech out to the rest of the class. Would they be persuaded by your argument?

List

1   Imagine you are a foster parent. List the qualities you would look for in an evacuee.

2   What sort of child would you wish to avoid? Make a list of your reasons.

Discuss

1   Look carefully at this photograph of a group of evacuees.
    Imagine you are able to look after two of them. Which two would you choose and why?

2   Which two would you definitely not choose? Why?

Talk and Write

Work in small groups.

1   First of all, on your own, imagine that you are one of the children in this photograph. Choose a name, age, and identity for yourself. Write a description for your foster parents telling them something about you, your family, your home, your likes and dislikes, etc. Before you start writing, you may prefer to work with your group and use the hot seating technique described on page 86 to help you create your character.

2   Swap your written descriptions with another group.

3   Now, imagine you are foster parents. Read the descriptions you have been given and choose one or two children to take into your home.

4   Then, tell the rest of the class whom you have chosen and why.

Research

Try to find out some true stories about children who were evacuated. You may have relatives or family friends who were evacuees or whose family acted as foster parents. Interview them about their experiences. If you are unable to find anyone who had a personal experience of being evacuated, you will be able to find factual books on the evacuation. Ask your librarian for help.

Research and Write

More about the Second World War

You may want to find out more about life during the Second World War. Research and then write an encyclopedia entry for a CD Rom for one or more of the following subjects:

- evacuees at home
- evacuees sent abroad
- rationing
- identity cards
- personal food allowances
- the black market
- the value of old money
- extra rations (this began in November 1941)
- the 'Dig for Victory' campaign
- clothes rationing
- wartime recipes

Further Reading

The following books are worth looking out for:

No Time to Wave Goodbye and *The Day They Took the Children* by Ben Wicks, both published by Bloomsbury.

How they Lived – A Schoolchild in World War II by Miriam Moss, published by Wayland.

The Home Front: Evacuation by Fiona Reynaldson, published by Wayland.

In addition to reading the novel of **Carrie's War**, you might want to try *Goodnight Mister Tom* by Michelle Magorian, published by Puffin and *War Boy* by Michael Foreman, published by Pavillion Books, and in paperback by Puffin.

A librarian will be able to suggest other works of fiction set during the Second World War.

Drama

You can use the following drama techniques to help you to explore the play further.

Still Image
A still image is like a photograph. Any number of people may be in the image. A situation is chosen and the group must produce a frozen picture as if they had just been captured on film by a photographer. You may wish to choose just one image or use a series of images to tell a story.

Thought Tapping
This helps us to understand what the characters in a still image are thinking. In turn, each member of the group says what their character was thinking at the moment the 'photograph' was taken.

Still Image

1   In groups of five or six, create the story of a group of children being evacuated, by producing the following three still images.
   ● The evacuees saying goodbye to their parents.
   ● The evacuees travelling on a train or bus.
   ● The evacuees waiting to be chosen by foster parents.
   Remember, not every member of the group has to be in every still image.

Thought Tapping

2   Give each character in the image a thought that they are thinking at the moment captured by the image. Do this for all three images. Show your three images to the rest of the class.

Hot Seating
When a member of the group has played or is about to play a character in an improvisation, a rôle play, or a written play, they can be put in the 'hot seat'. This means that other members of the group can ask them questions, and they must answer them **in the character** of their chosen person.

Hot Seating

1   Prepare a list of questions to ask Carrie, Nick, and Albert about their experience of being evacuees. You may want to use the questions below as a starting point.
   ● What did you think when you were told that you were being evacuated?
   ● Have you been scared or lonely in Wales? If so, why?
   ● What were your first impressions of Wales?
   ● What did you think of the people in Wales?

2   Choose members of the class to play the parts of Carrie, Nick, and Albert and 'hot seat' them.

3   Prepare a list of questions to ask other characters in the play.

4   Choose more members of the class to play these parts and 'hot seat' them too.

Improvisation
You are given a situation to work on in groups. Using your own words, you act out a scene which shows what you think about the subject. There are two main types of improvisation.

Planned: in this you are given time to prepare your work by talking with your friends and trying out your ideas. When you have practised your work and are satisfied with it, you show it to other people.

Instant: in this you are given a character and a situation, but you are not given any time to prepare. You must start the improvisation straight away.

Discuss

For many evacuees, evacuation was the first time they had ever been out of the city into the countryside and seen animals such as cows and sheep! For children in the villages, the arrival of the evacuees would also have been a big event. In the novel **Carrie's War**, Nina Bawden makes no reference to Carrie or Nick meeting any local children. Why do you think this is?

Improvise 1 Improvise a scene where Carrie, Nick and Albert meet a group of village children. Both sets of youngsters are curious about each other, but they are also wary. You may want to use the questions below as a starting point.
   ● What happens?
   ● What questions might they ask each other?
   ● Will they understand each other's accents?
   ● Will they get on or will a confrontation develop?

Think about the differences there might have been between living in the country and living in the city during wartime. Try to bring these differences into your improvisation.

2 Mr Evans is very strict in deciding what Carrie and Nick can and cannot eat. Although Nick moans about not having a turkey at Christmas, and claims he was hungry when he stole the biscuits, he generally likes the food that he is given. However, many real-life evacuees were not so lucky. In small groups, improvise a scene in which an evacuee is taken to a foster home. For their first meal, they are given something to eat that they loathe. How does the evacuee deal with this situation?

Characters

Character Studies

Talk and Write

1   Choose one of the following characters from the playscript:
    - Carrie Willow
    - Nick Willow
    - Albert Sandwich
    - Mr Evans
    - Auntie Lou
    - Hepzibah Green

2   Make a list of words that describe them.

3   Then look for examples that back up the words you have chosen. For instance, if you think that Carrie is kind, find an incident in the play that supports this viewpoint.

Read

The people in the play have different opinions about each other. By looking at what they say about each other, we can build up a greater understanding of each individual character.

Talk and Write

1   Make a list of the good and the bad things that the different characters in the play say about Mr Evans. It has been started for you.

BAD THINGS

Who says it	What they say
Nick	He's mean and nasty
Mrs Gotobed	Cold, hard, mean man

GOOD THINGS

Who says it	What they say
Adult Carrie	Mr Evans was honest

2   When you have finished the list, look at it, and answer the following questions.
    - What does this tell you about Mr Evans?
    - What does it tell you about the other characters?
    - Do any of the characters change their opinion of Mr Evans? If so, why?
    - Does this help your understanding of the characters in the play?
    - How do you personally feel towards Mr Evans at the end of the play?
    - Do you think he deserves what happens to him at the end of the play? If so, why? If not, why not?

3   Make a similar list for other characters in the playscript, for example:
- Mrs Gotobed
- Hepzibah Green
- Carrie
- Nick
- Auntie Lou

4   Discuss your findings with other members of the class.

Write

1   Imagine you are Carrie or Nick. Write a letter to your mother in Glasgow, telling her how you are getting on in Wales. Tell her about the people you have met and the things you are doing.

2   Now write an extract from your personal diary of your time in Wales. This may cover several specific incidents that take place, or a period of time, for example: the first days of your stay or the Christmas holidays.

3   In what ways is the diary different to the letter that you write?

Talk and Write

Mr Evans

1   Mr Evans has certain rules that he expects Carrie and Nick to follow. Go through the playscript and make a list of these. Look especially at Scenes 2 and 3.

2   Look at your list of Mr Evans's rules. Decide which you think are reasonable and which are not. Try not to judge Mr Evans by today's standards. Remember to think about when and how he was brought up and also how people thought and acted during the war.

3   Now make a list of the 'rules' that your parents expect you to follow.

4   Compare this list with the list of Mr Evans's rules. Discuss the similarities and differences between the two lists with other members of the class.

5   Mr Evans also has certain attitudes towards women and children. Make a list of these.

6   Why would we consider these attitudes 'old fashioned' today?

Read and Discuss

Mister Johnny

1   Turn to the section, What the Adapter Says (page 78) and read what Robert Staunton says about his reasons for using a tailor's dummy to represent the character of Mister Johnny.

2   Do you think he is right to do this? Discuss your thoughts with other members of the class.

3   How do the other characters in the play react to Mister Johnny? What do they say about him?

4   Does this tell us anything about their own personalities?

Dilemmas

Carrie's 'war' is not only the one happening between Germany and Britain, but it is also about Carrie's personal feelings and the battles going on inside her. She has to make several important decisions during the play, choosing what she feels to be the best course of action.

Discuss

In small groups discuss why Carrie does the following:
- send Major Harper away? (Scene 9)
- not tell her mother the truth about Nick and Mr Evans? (Scene 3)
- not act as a spy for Mr Evans? (Scene 8)
- throw the skull into the pond? (Scene 12)
- eventually believe that Mr Evans did not take Mrs Gotobed's will?
- believe she is responsible for the fire at Druid's Bottom?

You could do this as a hot seating exercise (see page 86) by choosing someone to play Carrie and questioning her about her actions.

Discuss

Two Carries

1 How different are the characters of Adult Carrie and Carrie as a girl?
2 Why do you think Robert Staunton chose to have two Carries appearing together throughout the play?

Then and Now

Read

There is a great difference between the world of Carrie Willow and the world we live in today. In the section, What the Adapter Says, Robert Staunton writes: '**Carrie's War**... offers a valuable insight into the years of the Second World War and particularly daily life in the rural areas which had changed little since Victorian times.' The changes in the way we live today could probably never have been imagined in the 1930s and 40s.

Research and Write

1   Divide into small groups. Each group has responsibility for collecting information about the differences between the world of 1939-45 and the present day. You could explore the areas listed below:
    ● schools
    ● work
    ● clothes
    ● travel
    ● holidays
    ● inventions
    ● lifestyle
    ● the home

2   You might wish to collect pictures of the differences between the way people lived in the 1930s and 40s and the way we live today. You could even collect items from this period such as ration books, gas masks etc. Your local schools' museum service may be able to help you with these.

3   Then make up a 'Then and Now' display or exhibition. You might want to set things out like this.

ROADS

Then	Now
photos Roads in the 1930s (with few cars)	photos/pictures Huge motorway traffic jams

Picture This

Discuss

These photographs are from the original production of the playscript **Carrie's War**.

Read what Robert Staunton says in What the Adapter Says (page 78) to help you answer the following questions.

1   Who are the characters?
2   From which parts of the play are these photographs taken?
3   Explain your answers to other members of the class.

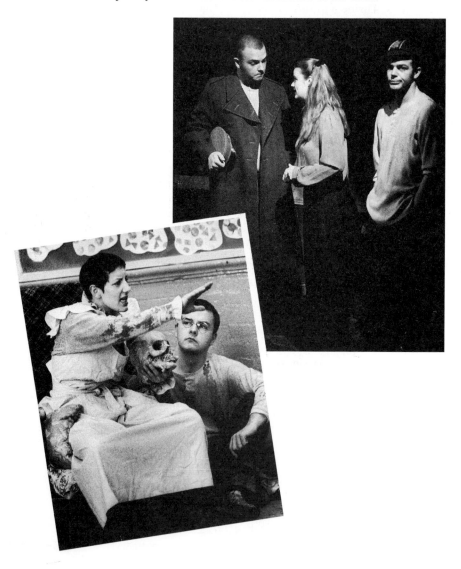

Staging

If a play is described as being naturalistic, it means that what happens on the stage is just like real life – people act 'naturally', the set looks 'normal', and people generally speak to each other as they would in real life.

Talk and Write

Would you describe this adaptation of **Carrie's War** as naturalistic? If not, why not? Discuss this in small groups and make a list of your reasons. You may want to refer to the section, What the Adapter Says, on page 78.

Read and Design

Putting on the Play
Read What the Adapter Says (page 78) and A Note on the Set (page 5). Using the information from these pages, design a set for a production of **Carrie's War** to take place at your school.

Design

Poster
Design a poster for a production of **Carrie's War**. You will need to think about the following things:
● what information you wish to convey
● how to make the poster eye-catching
● what images you want to use. Do you use drawings or actual pictures/photos from the 1930s and 40s or a mixture of both?

Draw

Costumes
Design some costumes for the characters in the play. You will need to find out what style of clothing was worn in the 1930s and 40s. You can research this in special costume history books or use photographs, video footage, or films of the time to help you.

Research

Music
You could use music in a production of **Carrie's War**. Try to listen to songs and music written during the war. These could be used as backing music. You should be able to find such songs in your local audio library. Your teachers or relatives may be able to help as well. Alternatively, you could compose your own backing track in order to help create a dramatic atmosphere.

Write

Props

If an actor is allowed one item of clothing or one prop to create their character, what would you give the following?

- Adult Carrie
- Carrie Willow
- Nick Willow
- Auntie Lou
- Mrs Willow
- Mr Evans
- Hepzibah Green
- Albert Sandwich
- Major Harper
- Mrs Gotobed
- Teacher

Remember, you will need to be able to identify each character by their clothing or prop. You may wish to look at the photographs from the original production on pages 92–93 to get some ideas.

Brainstorm

Exhibition

You could combine a performance of the play with an exhibition of wartime artefacts (see the section Then and Now on page 91). To add to the fun of the production, you might wish to have the ushers and ticket sellers dressed in period costume and serve food which was popular during the war years at the interval. Brainstorm some more ideas along these lines.

Mime

Mime Techniques

In Scene 5, page 31, Carrie and Nick have to 'walk' and 'run' during their trip to Druid's Bottom. Obviously, the characters cannot run for real on stage. Therefore you will have to use a mime technique. This is basically a 'running on the spot' exercise. Your legs and arms will be moving as if you were running, but your body remains at a fixed point on the stage. Greater realism can be created by one of the characters 'overtaking' the other by simply having that character move slowly forward a metre or so and the other character move slowly backwards. This pattern is then swapped over and repeated, giving the illusion of the characters 'racing' against each other in their desire to get away from the strange noise.

You could even mime the running in slow motion, although this is more difficult to keep up. Try some of these ideas out and experiment with some of your own. You may find a better way of doing it.

Plays in this series include:

Across the Barricades   ISBN 0 19 831272 5
  Joan Lingard   adapted by David Ian Neville

The Bonny Pit Laddie   ISBN 0 19 831278 4
  *Frederick Grice   adapted by David Spraggon Williams
                    with Frank Green*

The Burston School Strike   ISBN 0 19 831274 1
  Roy Nevitt

The Canterbury Tales   ISBN 0 19 831293 8
  Geoffrey Chaucer   adapted by Martin Riley

Carrie's War   ISBN 0 19 831295 4
  Nina Bawden   adapted by Robert Staunton

The Demon Headmaster   ISBN 0 19 831270 9
  Gillian Cross   adapted by Adrian Flynn

Frankenstein   ISBN 0 19 831267 9
  Mary Shelley   adapted by Philip Pullman

Hot Cakes   ISBN 0 19 831273 3
  Adrian Flynn

Jane Eyre   ISBN 0 19 831296 2
  Charlotte Brontë   adapted by Steve Barlow and Steve Skidmore

Johnny and the Dead   ISBN 0 19 831294 6
  Terry Pratchett   adapted by Stephen Briggs

Paper Tigers   ISBN 0 19 831268 7
  Steve Barlow and Steve Skidmore

A Question of Courage   ISBN 0 19 831271 7
  Marjorie Darke   adapted by Bill Lucas and Brian Keaney

Smith   ISBN 0 19 831297 0
  Leon Garfield   adapted by Robert Staunton

A Tale of Two Cities   ISBN 0 19 831292 X
  Charles Dickens   adapted by Steve Barlow and Steve Skidmore

Tigers on the Prowl   ISBN 0 19 831277 6
  Steve Barlow and Steve Skidmore

The Turbulent Term of Tyke Tiler   ISBN 0 19 831269 5
  adapted from her own novel by Gene Kemp